MACKENZIE DELTA:
Environmental Interactions and
Implications of Development

Editors

P. Marsh and C.S.L. Ommanney

Proceedings of the Workshop on the Mackenzie Delta, 17-18 October
1989, Saskatoon, Saskatchewan

National Hydrology Research Institute
Inland Waters Directorate
Conservation and Protection
Environment Canada

11 Innovation Boulevard
Saskatoon, Saskatchewan
Canada   S7N 3H5

NHRI Symposium No. 4

Cat. En 36-512/4E
ISSN 0838 1984
ISBN 0-662-17686-3

TABLE OF CONTENTS

SESSION 3: ENVIRONMENTAL CHANGE

OPENING REMARKS

The program for the next two days encompasses disciplines of geology, biology, hydrology, hydraulics, and sedimentology.

Having scientists bring their expertise to bear on a subject like this is becoming more and more essential. Environmental questions and their attendant socio-economic issues can no longer be considered in isolation. Sustainable development concepts now generally accepted, especially by D.O.E., demand such interactions.

I expect that more meetings like this will be necessary as no one Institute or organization is capable of making and/or maintaining sufficient scope in their investigations. It seems that we at NHRI as a government agency will often be the group which is able to play the role of instigating meetings to promote discussion and information exchange.

Man's activities impact or are impacted on by Meteorological Processes, Hydrological Processes and Biological Processes. All are to a greater or lesser degree interlinked.

The Delta as an environment provides a means to comprehend the complex interactions of development and natural processes.

The Delta is a significant resource, supports the lifestyle of the local population, and is a growing attraction for tourists. It is a potential source of oil and gas and may be threatened by its development and that of hydropower upstream.

Furthermore, global climate, i.e., shifts of averages, may change the local thermodynamic balance, the hydrological balance, the river flow, the sediment flow, the ice regime and the sea level.

The Delta therefore provides a major natural laboratory to look at all these interactions. The outcome of the Workshop is expected to be threefold:

1. *To improve communication and contacts between researchers from different disciplines.*

2. *To improve our appreciation of all the complex natural interactions and our ability to handle complex scientific and socio-economic issues.*

3. *To identify the issues and or problems which should receive attention in the future.*

Lastly, perhaps this Workshop should be a catalyst to create a response and to revitalize the Mackenzie River Basin Committee. Perhaps it's because of the size of the river, the scope of formal activity should also encompass the Beaufort Sea which receives the outflow. It is quite evident that in the long run the Mackenzie Basin system will encounter stresses and alterations because of development. Tools and understanding to handle this, need to be developed before the event.

Developing resources without losing the primitive character of the region which is a major attraction for certain tourists remains a significant challenge.

The papers proposed look interesting and should provoke discussion. After two days, we should be able to comment better on the need for future action and future collaboration.

T.M. Dick, Director

National Hydrology Research Institute
Environment Canada
Saskatoon, Saskatchewan, S7N 3H5

17 October 1989

THE MACKENZIE DELTA: THE RESEARCH CHALLENGE

by P. Marsh

Chairman, Scientific Programme committee
Mackenzie Delta Workshop
National Hydrology Research Institute
11 Innovation Boulevard
Saskatoon, Saskatchewan, S7N 3H5

INTRODUCTION

For generations, many Canadians have taken the remote, wilderness locations of their country for granted, assuming that they are unaffected by southern industrial activity and will retain their unique, natural conditions indefinitely. During the last decade, however, the public has become increasingly conscious of, and concerned about, environmental problems. Canadians now realize that their wilderness areas are indeed vulnerable to environmental degradation. They demand information on the environmental effects of new ventures and closely scrutinize them. The public is also becoming concerned about the implications of global environmental problems such as climate change, rising sea-level, ozone depletion, and the long-range transport of pollutants. In response to both local and global concerns, the public, policy makers and political leaders are looking to scientists for advice.

One area in northern Canada where the environment is of great importance is the Mackenzie Delta. Here there is a need for scientists to provide accurate, long-term predictions of environmental change. This Delta, located where the Mackenzie River empties into the Beaufort Sea, is the tenth largest delta in the world. Of arctic deltas, it is the largest in North America, and second only to the Lena River Delta in Siberia. Deltas, such as the Mackenzie Delta, are "ecologically rich landforms noted for their economic import and vulnerability" (DELTA, 1990) and therefore require special attention.

The public often assumes that scientists can answer complex environmental questions. However, this is not always the case. For example, the current suite of questions being posed about the Mackenzie Delta require an understanding of the interactions between all portions of the environment; the atmosphere, oceans, hydrosphere, and biosphere. Unfortunately, past studies have not provided scientists with adequate knowledge of these complex interactions. The research challenge facing scientists is to develop the scientifically rigorous methods required for predicting environmental change so that the appropriate responses can be implemented before serious environmental problems occur.

THE MACKENZIE DELTA WORKSHOP - ENVIRONMENTAL INTERACTIONS AND EFFECTS OF DEVELOPMENT

Given the importance of the Mackenzie Delta, it was appropriate to bring together scientists and managers to discuss past research efforts, the current state of our knowledge, and future research directions. The primary aim was to attract scientists from various disciplines to discuss interactions between different elements of the physical and biological environments.

These proceedings are the formal record of the workshop held at the National Hydrology Research Centre in October 1989. The published papers are not a comprehensive review of past research, but are a snapshot of current investigations in the area, brief discussions of future research requirements, and a source of references for those with an interest in the Mackenzie Delta.

Besides the formal papers, there was much discussion during the workshop on research needs; on which some workshop participants later elaborated. The following sections are neither a comprehensive summary of the discussions at the workshop nor those following it. Rather, they are personal impressions of past research directions and current needs, flavoured by discussions at the workshop and information subsequently received.

ENVIRONMENTAL CONCERNS AND RELATED RESEARCH ACTIVITIES

Unlike many of the world's great deltas, the Mackenzie Delta is virtually pristine. Environmental degradation is a major concern of those who depend on the Delta for food, for revenue from fishing, hunting, trapping and tourism, and those who wish to preserve unique landscapes and ecosystems in Canada. Over the past 20 years, there have been a number of proposals for industrial development, either within the Delta or upstream on the Mackenzie River, which might result in serious environmental problems. As well, there are concerns about the potential effects of global change. These, and a brief summary of previous research activities associated with them, are discussed below.

Oil and Gas Development

The prospect of oil and gas development in the Mackenzie Delta and Beaufort Sea has stimulated considerable study of possible environmental effects. During the 1970s, many investigations were carried out under the auspices of the "Environmental-Social Program - Northern Pipelines". As described by Hunt *et al.* (1974), research covered the northern Yukon, Mackenzie Delta, and Mackenzie Valley regions, and dealt with many aspects of the physical and biological environment. Because of the overall lack of information, these were not integrated environmental studies and tended to be preliminary in nature. Oil and gas development in the Delta was also addressed by the Canadian Arctic Resources Committee (1977).

After this early, intensive program, the amount of research decreased following the 1977 Berger Commission report which recommended a 10-year postponement of a Mackenzie Valley pipeline (Berger, 1977). During the mid- and late-1980s, research activity again increased in the Mackenzie Delta region, this time funded primarily by the Northern Oil and Gas Action Program (NOGAP). This program did not try to complete an integrated understanding of the delta system, but addressed specific concerns related to oil and gas development (i.e., Canada, DIAND, 1990).

Hydro-electric Development

During the early 1980s B.C. Hydro proposed building a hydro-electric dam on the Liard River (B.C. Hydro, 1985). The resulting impact study was based on the realization that the Mackenzie Delta was "a complex, interactive ecosystem, and that study integration was essential" (Wilkins and Hirst, 1991). No previous study had taken this approach to an impact assessment of the Delta. However, B.C. Hydro limited even these studies to those aspects of the Delta which they felt would most likely be affected by hydro-electric development. For example, as Wilkins and Hirst point out, the permafrost regime of the Delta was omitted because it was felt that it would not be affected by hydro development.

The B.C. Hydro investigations led to many reports on different aspects of the Delta (see Wilkins and Hirst, this volume for a list of B.C. Hydro reports). However, with the cancellation of the Liard dam proposal in the mid-1980s, B.C. Hydro ceased all studies related to it, so no integrating analysis was published. To summarize the findings, former B.C. Hydro employees completed a report for the Federal Government (Hirst *et al.*, 1987). This is the most detailed, integrated study of the delta ecosystem so far, but it is insufficient to predict the effect of a disturbance on the Delta.

Global Warming

Current Global Circulation Models (i.e., Boer *et al.*, 1990) predict increased global temperatures, with the warming being greater in northern latitudes. If warming occurs, the Mackenzie Delta would be affected by changes in local climate, discharge from the Mackenzie and Peel Rivers, ice-jam induced floods, sea-level, and sediment input to the Delta. Some preliminary work considers the consequences for individual aspects of the Delta (e.g., Marsh, 1991), but the effects on the entire ecosystem are unknown and unpredictable at present.

Long Range Transport of Toxics

Numerous studies (i.e., Barrie, 1986) show that the arctic air mass contains significant levels of anthropogenic pollutants. For example, Barrie (1986) showed that from January to April, 1980, the ground-level concentration of sulphate in the atmosphere was as high in the Mackenzie Delta region as in southern Ontario. The dominant source area for such atmospheric pollutants in northern Canada is Eurasia (Barrie, 1986). Toxics may also be transported down the Mackenzie River and into the Delta. Although Nagy *et al.* (1987) looked at the movement of hydrocarbons along the Mackenzie, the transport of other toxics has not received much attention. Recent proposals for pulp mills on the Peace and Athabasca Rivers, in northern Alberta, raised the awareness of this problem. Despite the assumption that Lake Athabasca and Great Slave Lake will remove toxics, thus 'protecting' downstream areas such as the Mackenzie Delta, this has not been thoroughly examined. In addition, no studies have considered the implications of these, or other, pollutants for the Mackenzie Delta ecosystem.

Given these environmental concerns, we need accurate, scientifically-rigorous, techniques for predicting likely changes in the Mackenzie Delta ecosystem. Previous work directed at specific proposals failed to produce the comprehensive understanding of the delta system required. Development of these methods is a major scientific challenge.

RESEARCH NEEDS

The greatest limitation to previous research programmes such as those described above, is that they focused on single problems or issues, not generally-applicable, integrated studies. Although this approach has accomplished much and has greatly improved our knowledge of the delta system, it has not provided a comprehensive understanding of the delta ecosystem. We need basic studies emphasizing the interaction between the physical and biological components of the ecosystem. Then we could better assess the problems as they arise.

Given the existing deficiencies, there is a need for continued studies including:

(1) **Baseline data:** to describe the natural variability of the present system, and for model testing. This includes:

(a) Hydrological and climatic data - although collected for many years, they have two limitations. First, they are of relatively short duration, with hydrological records covering only the period since 1972. Second, the spatial coverage of variability over the entire Delta is inadequate. The existing data collection must be maintained and expanded to provide improved spatial and temporal representation. Innovative techniques should be applied to improve certain aspects of the data base; for example, to the measurement of water-levels and discharge during break-up, and the measurement of snowfall.

(b) Biological data - there is also a need for baseline data on fish, muskrat, bird populations, and vegetation types in order to understand the relationship between the physical and biological components of the system. Although a number of agencies and research groups collect baseline data in the delta region, it is usually targeted at specific developments. As a result, the data cover limited areas and time periods. This deficiency should be corrected.

(c) Sea-level data - the record at Tuktoyaktuk must be continued, and new methods developed to ensure continuous records during the ice-covered period.

(2) **Paleo data:** to put present conditions in the context of longer-term variations. They are essential if we wish to understand how the Delta responds to natural, long-term variations in climate, and whether the short historical record represents longer-term conditions. Some of the information required includes:

(a) lake-sediment cores to provide information on: long-term variations in lake sedimentation; channel water-levels; and Mackenzie and Peel River discharge.

(b) tree-ring analysis to determine variations in local climate.

(c) deep sediment cores, such as those obtained by Johnston and Brown (1965), for a variety of delta locations. These are required to establish the evolutionary sequence of the Delta, including variations in sediment supply, and response to changing sea-level.

(3) **"Process" studies:** to understand basic conditions in the Delta. These include:

(a) the effect of ice cover, especially during break-up, on water-levels and channel flows.

(b) information on critical habitats and migration behaviour of various populations of coregonid species.

(c) spatial variations in the flooding regime and water balance of delta lakes to determine the viability of delta lakes given changes in climate and/or flooding.

(d) rates of sediment transport into and out of the Delta, and erosion/deposition rates within the Delta. This is especially critical for predicting changes in sedimentation in response to changes in flow regime.

(e) improved understanding of the permafrost regime in the Delta. This would include: the ice content of the top of the permafrost; rates of permafrost growth in new sediments; thermokarst processes on channel and lake banks, and determining why permafrost in the modern Delta is warmer than nearby areas outside the Delta.

(f) bio-geochemical processes in delta lakes, emphasizing the cycling of nutrients between the Mackenzie River and lakes, and the role of land drainage and atmospheric inputs. This is required for predicting changes in delta productivity.

(g) rates of natural and anthropogenic toxic input (atmospheric and riverine) to the Delta, accumulation of toxics in various delta ecosystems, and their long-term effects.

(h) sea-level rise and land subsidence.

(i) processes controlling lake development and destruction; reflecting the long-term stability of delta lakes and their probable response to changing climate.

(4) **Integrated ecosystem studies and model development**: to answer important questions concerning environmental change by integrating existing and proposed studies and developing linked models. Although those discussed above are considered essential, and will provide an improved understanding of the Delta, by themselves they cannot predict the consequences of global change. There is a great need to integrate these studies in order to determine the linkages between various aspects of the ecosystem. Some parts of the system which must be modelled interactively include:

(a) discharge into the Delta - through a macro-scale hydrological model capable of predicting flows from the Mackenzie and Peel Rivers. This is the long-term goal of the Global Energy and Water Experiment (GEWEX) (see GEWEX News, 1991).
(b) freeze-up ice-cover conditions and ice jams in the Delta.
(c) discharge and water-levels in the main delta channels under both open and ice-covered conditions: a flow routing model, such as the One-D Hydrodynamic Model (Sydor *et al.*, 1989), is required. However, this must be integrated with an ice component to predict conditions during the ice season.
(d) interaction between the biogeochemical and hydrological processes controlling the water and nutrient balance of the major ecosystems in the Delta.
(e) response of vegetation to climate, water-levels, sediment and nutrient inputs.
(f) population dynamics of fish, migrating birds and muskrat.

(5) **Comparative Studies**: to attain a broader understanding of those factors responsible for current conditions and the potential response of a delta to changes in climate or flow. Since the Mackenzie Delta is the only large arctic delta in Canada, there is limited opportunity for investigating other similar ecosystems and landforms. Because much of the work does not have general applicability, but is specific to the Mackenzie Delta, it is essential to carry out comparative studies. Deltas which would be suitable for this are the Lena River Delta and other smaller arctic deltas in the Soviet Union and Alaska.

Although individual agencies can do much of the work outlined above, the co-ordination needed to integrate ecosystem studies can best be achieved through a formal study. There are a number of relevant national and international studies currently being planned that may provide an appropriate structure for co-ordinated delta studies. These include:

(a) the Canadian Global Change Program (CGCP) (see DELTA, 1990). The Royal Society of Canada is co-ordinating global change activity in Canada through the

CGCP. The International Geosphere-Biosphere Program (IGBP), one part of this program, will "describe and understand the interactive physical, chemical and biological processes that regulate the total Earth system, the unique environment that it provides for life, the changes that are occurring in this system, and the manner in which they are influenced by human actions". Since the CGCP could provide the framework for an integrated investigation of the Mackenzie Delta, and such a study would make an important contribution to the CGCP, there should be a concerted effort to ensure that this occurs.

(b) the Mackenzie Basin Impact Study (see Cohen, 1991). While not focused solely on the Delta, this framework would encourage collaboration in delta studies.

(c) the Global Energy and Water Experiment. It is proposed that one aspect of the Canadian contribution to GEWEX will focus on the Mackenzie Basin. In conjunction with international GEWEX activities, this program may result in a macro-scale hydrological model capable of predicting discharge from the Mackenzie Basin. Although this may not have a direct impact on delta research, it will lead to an increased understanding of the natural and anthropogenic changes in discharge into the Mackenzie Delta.

ACKNOWLEDGEMENTS

The success of the Mackenzie Delta Workshop was due to the hard work of a number of people. I would like to thank: my co-editor Simon Ommanney for his editorial assistance in ensuring a consistent and professional publication; Karen Ulmer for producing the final text of the proceedings; Sherri Salmond for reformatting the original documents; Phil Gregory for modifying the graphics where necessary, designing the cover and for final production of the proceeding; Tracey Scheller for providing additional graphics support; Karen Morin for secretarial support and work at the reception desk; Kevin Kuit and Mike McPhee for making the local arrangements; Art Dalton for audio-visual assistance at the workshop; Brenda Doell for co-ordinating workshop registration; and NHRI for funding the workshop and production of the proceedings. Finally, I would like to thank all of the session chairmen and authors who were ultimately responsible for the success of the meeting.

REFERENCES

BARRIE, L.A., 1986. Arctic air pollution: an overview of current knowledge. Atmospheric Environment, 20(4), 643-663

B.C. HYDRO, 1985. Liard River development. Downstream hydrology: interim report. Report No.H-1794, Hydroelectric Generation Projects Division, B.C. Hydro, Vancouver, British Columbia, March, 191 pp. + 44 figs

BERGER, T.R., 1977. Northern Frontier, Northern Homeland: the report of the Mackenzie Valley Pipeline Inquiry: Volume 1. Ministry of Supply and Services Canada, Ottawa, Ontario, 213 pp.

BOER, G.J., N. McFARLANE, J.-P. BLANCHET and M. LAZARE, 1990. Greenhouse gas induced climatic change simulated with the CCC second generation GCM. In - Application of the Canadian Climate Centre General Circulation Model Output for Regional Climate Impact Studies: Guidelines for Users, Canadian Climate Centre, Atmospheric Environment Service, Downsview, Ontario, April, 2-5

CANADA, DIAND, 1990. NOGAP project progress reports. Department of Indian Affairs and Northern Development, Ottawa, Ontario.

CANADIAN ARCTIC RESOURCES COMMITTEE, 1977. Mackenzie Delta - priorities and alternatives. Conference Proceedings, 3-4 December 1975, Ottawa, Ontario, Canadian Arctic Resources Committee, 193 pp.

COHEN, S.J. 1991. Regional impacts of projected global warming: a research proposal for the Mackenzie Basin. Preprints, 2nd Symposium on Global Change Studies, 14-18 January 1991, New Orleans, Louisiana, American Meteorological Society, 74-77

DELTA, 1990. The CGCP. DELTA, Newsletter of the Canadian Global Change Program, 1(2), Royal Society of Canada, 13 pp.

GEWEX NEWS, 1991. Global Energy and Water Cycle Experiment News, 1(1). World Climate Research Programme, 8 pp.

HIRST, S.M., M. MILES, S.P. BLACHUT, L.A. GOULET and R.E. TAYLOR, 1987. Quantitative synthesis of the Mackenzie Delta ecosystems. Applied Ecology Ltd., North Vancouver, B.C. for Inland Waters Directorate, Western and Northern Region, Conservation and Protection, Environment Canada, Edmonton, Alberta, December, main volume, 407 pp.; appendices, 141 pp.

HUNT, A.D., G.M. MacNABB and J.S. TENER, 1974. Mackenzie Valley and northern Yukon pipelines: socio-economic and environmental aspects. A report to the Task Force on Northern Oil Development, Government of Canada. Report No.74-17, Environmental-Social Committee, Northern Pipelines, Task Force on Northern Oil Development, Ottawa, Ontario, 197 pp.

JOHNSTON, G.H. and R.J.E. BROWN, 1965. Stratigraphy of the Mackenzie River Delta, Northwest Territories, Canada. Geological Society of America Bulletin, 76(1), 103-112

MARSH, P., 1991. Evaporation and ice growth in Mackenzie Delta lakes. Proceedings, Symposium on the Hydrology of Natural and Manmade Lakes, XX I.U.G.G. General Assembly, 11-24 August 1991, Vienna, Austria, IAHS Publication, International Association of Hydrological Sciences, in press

NAGY, E., J.H. CAREY, J.H. HART and E.D. ONGLEY, 1987. Hydrocarbons in the Mackenzie River. NWRI Contribution No.87-52, unpublished report, Lakes Research Branch, National Water Research Institute, Environment Canada, Burlington, Ontario, 7 pp. + tables and figures

SYDOR, M., G. BROWN, H. CHENG, W. BOUTOT and B. MORASSE, 1989. Getting the best of both worlds. Application of computer modelling in systems analysis: from micro to supercomputer. Preprint, 4th Canadian Seminar on Systems Theory for the Civil Engineer, 3-5 May 1989, University of Manitoba, Winnipeg, Manitoba, 15 pp.

WILKINS, S.P. and S.M. HIRST, 1991. Impact assessment of a complex ecosystem - The Mackenzie Delta. In - Mackenzie Delta: Environmental Interactions and Implications of Development, P. Marsh and C.S.L. Ommanney (Editors), Proceedings of the Workshop on the Mackenzie Delta, 17-18 October 1989, Saskatoon, Saskatchewan, NHRI Symposium No.4, National Hydrology Research Institute, Environment Canada, Saskatoon, Saskatchewan, 133-154

PHYSICAL PROCESSES

RECHARGE OF MACKENZIE DELTA LAKES DURING WINTER

C.R. Burn

Department of Geography
University of British Columbia
Vancouver, British Columbia
V6T 1W5   CANADA

ABSTRACT

Evidence of recharge to Mackenzie Delta lakes during winter was obtained in 1987-88 and 1988-89 at two sites near Inuvik, N.W.T. The lakes are connected to distributary channels throughout the summer, but drain during autumn as the Mackenzie stage falls. Lake-ice thickness and surface elevation were measured by chiselling holes in the ice and by levelling from a benchmark installed in permafrost. During winter 1987-88, the ice surface at both lakes rose after November. This was partly due to icing in December or January, but at one lake a further 31 cm were added to the ice and water column over the winter. About 20% of the increase in lake-ice level occurred during February and March. During 1988-89, the ice surface at this lake rose by 35 cm after December 10. Recharge of the lake during autumn, which may lead to icing, is probably due to ground-water discharge from the active layer before freeze-back is complete. Previously it was thought that further increase in lake level during winter was due to ground-water recharge from a talik connected with an aquifer flowing off the Caribou Hills. However, the increase in lake level is similar to the change in stage of the Mackenzie River gauged at Inuvik, suggesting that the East Channel backs up as delta outlets freeze through in mid- and late-winter and as channels become constricted by ice. Water may then re-enter some lakes from the delta channels.

INTRODUCTION

Studies of the frost-heave regime in lake-bottom sediments have been conducted at two sites in the Mackenzie Delta near Inuvik. Lake 1, close to "NRC" Lake, is 7-km southwest of Inuvik (Figure 1); Lake 2 is 16-km downstream from town along East Channel. Lake 2 is part of a cluster of lakes bounded to the east by the escarpment of the Caribou Hills. Both Lakes 1 and 2 are surrounded by permafrost, as are most lakes in the Mackenzie Delta (Mackay, 1963), and are connected to distributary channels of the Mackenzie River. In mid-September, a small boat can enter each lake without difficulty, but by October or during freeze-up, as the Mackenzie stage falls, water drains from the lakes into the channels. Drainage ceases from the lakes when the outlets freeze through or the Mackenzie stage rises again.

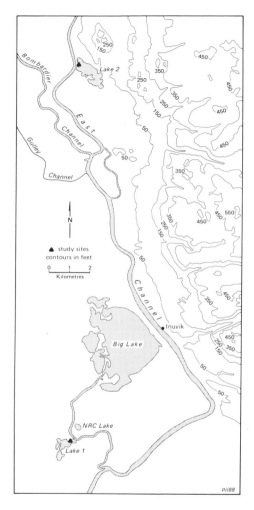

Figure 1. Location of study sites, Mackenzie Delta, Northwest Territories.

The primary objective of the fieldwork is to determine the magnitude and extent of frost heave in lake-bottom sediments of the Mackenzie Delta. This information may be required if pipelines are to traverse the Delta via a direct route rather than winding around lakes. The fine-grained nature of the sediments, their saturated condition, and the length of the freezing season lead to considerable ice segregation and frost heave in the annulus of each lake that freezes during winter (Burn, 1989).

As part of the measurement programme, surveys have been made of surface elevation and ice thickness at the lakes. These data allow some observations of the hydrology of delta lakes during winter. In this paper evidence for lake recharge during winter, and some observations of associated development of intrusive ice in lake sediments are presented.

FIELD METHODS

Field studies were conducted at Lakes 1 and 2 during winter 1987-88, and at Lake 2 in 1988-89. Overflow in delta channels prevented access by skidoo to Lake 1 before February during 1988-89. In 1987-88 field visits were made in late-November, January and March. During 1988-89, visits were in early-November, December, February and April.

Lake-ice thickness and surface elevation were measured during field visits by chiselling holes in the ice and by levelling from benchmarks installed in permafrost. The benchmarks comprise 0.5-in (12.7-mm) steel rods, 3.5-m long, covered in the active layer and near-surface permafrost by 2-m long sleeves of close-fitting aluminum tubing. Collars on the rods protruded into permafrost. It is assumed that the benchmarks heaved little: field checking in September 1989 indicated that the benchmarks had not been jacked out of the ground during the previous 24 months.

Lake-ice elevation was levelled at points marked by dowels along transects from shoreline. Tin cans frozen to the lake surface were used as level markers to provide a stable reference position at each site. In addition, during 1987-88, measurements of changes in lake level were obtained from sets of concentric heave tubes and magnet heavemeters installed at points where the water column did not freeze through (Mackay *et al.*, 1979; Mackay and Leslie, 1987). Changes in lake elevation were determined from the outermost heave tube, which was frozen to lake ice, and moved with the lake surface. Ring magnets were placed on the ice surface and on bottom sediment. The separation of these magnets, determined by a reed switch lowered down an access tube passing through the magnets, also indicated changes in lake level. The precision of measurement by levelling was approximately 1 cm, but observations of ± 0.1 mm were obtained from the heave tubes, and ± 0.5 mm from magnets.

Overflow at the lakes was measured on snow stakes installed during the first visit of each year.

RESULTS

Lake 1

During winter 1987-88, levelling surveys indicated an increase in ice-surface elevation between November and March of 7.5 cm. The final ice thickness at Lake 1 was 62 cm comprising 8 cm of icing, 28 cm of ice present in November and 27 cm formed from the 25 cm of the November water column (Table 1). The levelling and direct measurements are therefore in close agreement. Lake level declined by over 50 cm during freeze-up, as indicated by shell ice in certain parts of the lake, but drainage ceased after November to confine lake water and create conditions conducive to ice rupture. In aggregate terms, the lake surface did not move between November 19 and January 26, but at some point during this period lake drainage ceased and the lake ice ruptured, leading to icing. The ice surface rose between January and March by 7.5 cm.

Table 1. Changes in thickness of ice and water column over winter 1987-88 at Lake 1.

DATE	NOVEMBER 19, 1987	MARCH 19, 1988
Icing	0	8
Lake Ice	28	54
Water	25	0
Total (Ice & Water)	55	62

Note: Total is computed as if all column were ice.

Lake 2

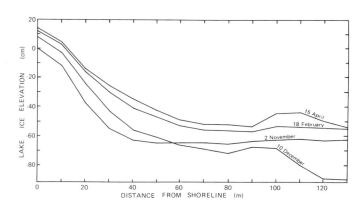

Figure 2. Changes in ice-surface elevation at Lake 2, winter 1988-89. Arbitrary zero is the shoreline on November 2, 1988. Measurements were made by levelling from a benchmark frozen in permafrost.

Changes in lake-ice elevation at Lake 2 over winter 1988-89 are indicated on Figure 2. Surveys were made on November 2, December 10, February 18 and April 15. Drainage of the lake during November and early-December lowered the surface level in the main body of the lake by 27 cm from the position on November 2. During this period, the ice surface between 0 and 50 m, where the water column had frozen through, was lifted by heaving in sub-ice sediments.

Between December 10 and February 18 the ice surface, at points where the ice was not grounded, rose by 35 cm. This occurred after frost had penetrated underlying sediment up to 90 m from the shoreline, since surface ice thickness did not change after December 10 between 0 and 90 m. The ice surface continued to rise after February 18, but at a lower rate.

Changes in lake-ice and water-column thickness during 1988-89 are in general agreement with levelled changes in lake elevation (Table 2). The agreement from month-to-month is not precise, probably due to undulations in the lake bottom, since holes were not re-opened for measurement. However, over the winter the agreement is good. The ice surface in mid-April was approximately 10-cm higher than during early-November.

During 1987-88 surveys at Lake 2 were made on November 23, January 23 and March 20. During the two months preceeding January 23 the ice surface at sites which were not grounded rose by 38 cm. Seventeen cm of icing (aufeis) were formed in the same period. In the subsequent two months the ice surface rose by a further 11 cm, but no more icing was noticed. All measurement techniques (levelling, magnets, heave tubes and direct measurement) were within 1 cm in estimating the increase in ice thickness.

Table 2. Changes (cm) in lake-ice elevation and thickness of water and ice at Lake 2, winter 1988-89.

LEVEL	NOV.2	DEC.10	FEB.18	APR.15	NOV.2 - APR.15
Lake-ice elevation	-63	-90	-56	-55	
Change	-	-27	+34	+1	+8

DIRECT MEASUREMENT	NOV.2	DEC.10	FEB.18	APR.15	NOV.2 - APR.15
Ice Depth	28	47	62	77	+49
Water Depth	54	17	31	14	-40
Total	82	64	93	91	
Change	-	-18	+29	-2	+9

Table 3 indicates the change in ice thickness between November 23 and March 20. The 89 cm of ice measured on March 20 comprised: 30 cm present in November; 17 cm of icing; 11 cm from freezing of 10 cm of water present in the November column; and 31 cm added to the ice cover below the lake surface. The icing and 31 cm added to the ice cover below the surface imply that 44 cm of water were added to the lake over the period.

The ground ice equivalent of the lower 31 cm added to the lake ice is intrusive ice, formed where water is injected under pressure into a freezing soil or rock. In the present case, the elevated water pressure raised the lake ice; with intrusive ground ice, an overlying layer of frozen soil is lifted by elevated pore-water pressures and bulk water is injected.

Intrusive Ice

Lake sediments were drilled in March 1988 and 1989 to determine ground-ice contents. In 1988, close to the limit of grounded ice, an ice lens 14-cm thick was observed 13-cm below the lake bottom. The lens comprised columnar vertical crystals 1 cm in diameter, with

Table 3. Change in thickness of ice and water column over winter 1987-88 in Lake 2, at a site where the water column did not freeze through.

DATE	NOVEMBER 23, 1987	MARCH 20, 1988
Icing	0	17
Lake Ice	30	72
Water	15	5
Total (Ice & Water)	46	94

Note: Total is computed as if all column were ice.

5

Burn

elongated bubbles up to 1-cm long. The lens was devoid of mineral inclusions. Ice-bonded sediments, 7-cm thick, lay below the ice lens. When these were penetrated, water rose to within 8 cm of the surface of the lake ice.

The hydrostatic head in the lake-sediment water and the form of the lens suggest it was intrusive ice, formed from water injected towards the freezing front. The large columnar crystals imply that the ice formed from bulk water, rather than by ice segregation.

Only traces of columnar ice, in lenses less than 1-cm thick, were recovered during drilling at similar locations in 1989.

DISCUSSION

During 1987-88, lake-ice rupture and icing were observed at both Lakes 1 and 2. In each case, the icing occurred in December or January. At Lake 1, it is attributed to active-layer discharge before freeze-back had been completed, but after the channel outlet had sealed.

Previously it was suggested that the increase in lake-surface elevation at Lake 2 during the winter might be due to continuing ground-water discharge through the lake talik into the water body (Burn, 1989). As indicated above, Lake 2 is part of a system of lakes bounded to the east by the escarpment of the Caribou Hills (Figure 1). Ground water may be expected to flow from the hills towards the lake system and to recharge the basin. Lake-ice rupture and overflow of discoloured water at "Red" Lake near Reindeer Station, 30-km north of Lake 2, is attributed to discharge of ground water through or below permafrost (J.R. Mackay, pers. comm., 1988). If recharge continues after the outlet to East Channel has frozen through and the lake basin is sealed, then lake water pressure may rise, lake ice may be raised, and, possibly, may rupture.

This interpretation is consistent with observations that:

(1)   The rate of ground-water recharge declines over winter (Table 4): active-layer discharge ceases, and aquifer recharge in permafrost regions is lowest during this season, leading to slower flow of deeper ground water (Williams, 1970).

(2)   A smaller increase in surface elevation occurred in 1988-89 than during 1987-88 because the water level at freeze-up was higher in 1988-89. As a result, closure of the outlet took longer, and discharge of ground water directly into the channel was prolonged.

Calculations of ground-water discharge rate into Lake 2 during both winters are similar (Table 4), further supporting the hypothesis, since ground-water movement is reasonably constant from year-to-year. In addition, the continuing elevation of the

Table 4. Recharge rates of Lake 2 during winters 1987-88 and 1988-89.

1987-88	NOV.24 - JAN.23	JAN.23 - MAR.20
mm·d^{-1}	5.7	1.9
cm·s^{-1}	6.6 x 10^{-6}	2.2 x 10^{-6}

1988-89	DEC.10 - FEB.18	FEB.18 - APR.15
mm·d^{-1}	4.9	0.2
cm·s^{-1}	5.6 x 10^{-6}	0.2 x 10^{-6}

Note: Method of calculation presented in Burn (1989, p.88).

ice surface throughout the winter at Lake 2, but terminating by January at Lake 1, may be a result of the regional groundwater gradient. The gradient may be steeper at Lake 2, close to the Caribou Hills, than at Lake 1 some distance from the edge of the Delta.

However, inspection of the East Channel stage records for 1987-88 suggests that ground water may not be responsible entirely for recharge of such lake basins during winter. Water Survey of Canada records indicate that the Mackenzie stage rose continuously during winter 1987-88 after December 14. In general, discharge declined, implying that water velocity decreased. The increase in stage is presumably a result of closure or constriction of channels in the Delta due to development of the ice cover.

Comparison of the stage records for 1987-88 with lake surface surveys indicates a close correspondence (Table 5). Therefore the increase in surface elevation of the lake may be due to refilling by channel water. In this case, the outlet would not have sealed, and a sub-ice channel between Lake 2 and East Channel would have remained open throughout the winter. Lake 1 may not have been affected to the same extent if the bottom of the outlet channel was, initially, above the stage.

It appears that the winter hydrology of these lakes may depend on the elevation of the outlet channel. This is similar to the analysis of summer flooding hydrology presented by Marsh and Hey (1989).

Table 5. Comparison of changes in the Mackenzie River (East Channel) stage at Inuvik and ice-surface level at Lake 2, winter 1987-88.

DATE	STAGE (m)	CHANGE OF STAGE (m)	CHANGE OF ICE LEVEL (m)
23 November	10.67	-	-
23 January	11.07	+0.40	+0.38
20 March	11.20	+0.13	+0.10

Notes: Data from Water Survey of Canada records. Mackenzie River stage at Inuvik is measured by a pneumatic gauge, relative to an arbitrary datum. Lake-ice level is measured relative to a benchmark anchored in permafrost.

CONCLUSIONS

There are two principal conclusions to be drawn from the observations that have been presented in this paper:

(1)   Discharge of near-surface ground water from the active layer may continue until January, and lead to overflow and icing once lake outlets have sealed and lake basins are confined.

(2)   Recharge of some lakes may occur during winter either as a result of ground-water discharge into the lake basin via a talik, or from streamflow into the lake body as the Mackenzie stage rises.

ACKNOWLEDGEMENTS

The study has been supported by the Geological Survey of Canada, Imperial Oil Limited and the Inuvik Research Centre.   Helpful suggestions regarding site selection were made by D.A. Sherstone, S.C. Bigras and M.E. Ferguson. Helpful discussions have been held with S.R. Dallimore, P.A. Egginton, J.R. Mackay and J.D. Ostrick.

REFERENCES

BURN, C.R., 1989. Frost heave of subaqueous lake-bottom sediments, Mackenzie Delta, Northwest Territories. In - Interior Plains and Arctic Canada, GSC Paper No.89-1D, Geological Survey of Canada, Ottawa, Ontario, 85-93

MACKAY, J.R., 1963. The Mackenzie Delta area, N.W.T. Geographical Branch Memoir No.8, Department of Mines and Technical Surveys, Ottawa, Ontario, 202 pp.

MACKAY, J.R. and R.V. LESLIE, 1987. A simple probe for the measurement of frost heave within frozen ground in a permafrost environment. In - Current Research, Part A, GSC Paper No.87-1A, Geological Survey of Canada, Ottawa, Ontario, 37-41

MACKAY, J.R., J. OSTRICK, C.P. LEWIS and D.K. MACKAY, 1979. Frost heave at ground temperatures below 0°C, Inuvik, Northwest Territories. In - Current Research, Part A, GSC Paper No.79-1A, Geological Survey of Canada, Ottawa, Ontario, 403-405

MARSH, P. and M. HEY, 1989. The flooding hydrology of Mackenzie Delta lakes near Inuvik, N.W.T., Canada. Arctic, 42(1), 41-49

WILLIAMS, J.R., 1970. Groundwater in permafrost regions of Alaska. U.S.G.S. Professional Paper No.696, United States Geological Survey, Washington, D.C., 83 pp.

SPATIAL VARIATIONS IN THE SPRING FLOODING OF MACKENZIE DELTA LAKES*

P. Marsh and M. Hey

National Hydrology Research Institute
11 Innovation Boulevard
Saskatoon, Saskatchewan
S7N 3H5   CANADA

ABSTRACT

The hydrological regime of the Mackenzie River is one of the major factors controlling the Mackenzie Delta ecosystem. For example, flooding by the Mackenzie River provides an important source of water, sediments, and nutrients to the delta lakes which cover approximately 25% of the delta surface. In spite of the importance of flooding to the productivity of delta lakes, little is known about the frequency or duration of lake flooding, or the spatial variation of these parameters. This deficiency makes it impossible to predict the effects of changes in the Mackenzie River hydrological regime on the lakes of the Mackenzie Delta. Changes in the Mackenzie regime could occur due to hydro-electric development, global warming, or rising sea level, for example.

In order to determine the frequency and duration of lake flooding and the spatial variations both within a small area and also on a north-south transect through the Delta, the sill elevations of 496 lakes were measured at three sites in the southern, central, and northern Delta. When these sill levels are compared to water-level records, it shows that the frequency of lake flooding varies greatly among the three study sites, with the frequency and duration of flooding increasing in a down-delta direction. These data have also allowed the quantification of a simple hydrological classification system. High-closure lakes, defined as those lakes which are not flooded annually in the spring, represent 13%, 33%, and 44% respectively of all lakes in the northern, central, and southern portions of the Delta.

INTRODUCTION

The Mackenzie Delta is covered by a vast network of interconnected lakes. These lakes occur at a range of elevations relative to the main river channels, from those at or below mean channel level to those perched a number of metres above mean channel level. This variation in sill level, where sill level is defined as the highest elevation along the connecting channel thalweg between the lake and dis-

*National Hydrology Research Institute Contribution Series Number CS-89077.

tributary channel (Marsh and Hey, 1989), has an important effect on the hydrological regime of these lakes. When the main channel level is above the sill elevation of any given lake, water floods into or out of the lake, depending on whether the main channel level is rising or falling. The resulting exchange of water, sediment, nutrients, and pollutants between lakes and channels has important effects on the lakes. Variations in main channel water levels, and therefore in lake inputs/outputs, are driven by (1) snowmelt or rainfall run-off in the Mackenzie basin, (2) ice jams in the Mackenzie Delta, and (3) storm surges in the Beaufort Sea.

Previous studies (Mackay, 1963; Gill, 1971; Hirst *et al.*, 1987; Bigras, 1990) have described the flooding regime of delta lakes, but they have been limited by the availability of only short-term data for only a few lakes. Marsh and Hey (1989) provided the first frequency analysis of lake flooding in the central Delta near Inuvik. This work used 20 years of main channel water-level data to determine the timing, duration, and return period of lake flooding and then classify lakes according to their flooding regime. However, this previous study only considered lakes in the central Delta near Inuvik. It did not provide information on the spatial variation in lake flooding regime in either down- or cross-delta directions. This paper will try to overcome part of this deficiency by providing preliminary data on the spring flooding regime for lakes in the southern (upper) and northern (lower) Delta and compare these to lakes in the central Delta as reported previously by Marsh and Hey (1989). Specifically, this paper will document the distribution of lake sill levels, and finally the frequency of lake flooding during the spring period at three sites along a 120-km north-south transect of the Mackenzie Delta.

STUDY AREA AND METHODOLOGY

The three study areas (marked by squares on Figure 1) include: the Gills Camp area just north of Reindeer Station, a central site near Inuvik (called "NRC Lake" area) described by Marsh and Hey (1989), and a southern site referred to as the "Dishwater Lake" area. This southern site is just north of the point where East Channel branches off from Middle Channel. The distance between each of these sites is approximately 60 km, for a total of 120 km within the 200-km N-S extent of the Mackenzie Delta. These study sites do not address the issue of cross-delta variations in flooding regime.

Since a ground survey of a large number of lake sill elevations was impossible, we utilized the areal survey technique described by Marsh and Hey (1989). This technique is based on the fact that with rising main-channel water levels, spring floodwater enters into lakes with progressively higher sills. Since Mackenzie floodwater is sediment laden, it is easy to distinguish floodwater from local meltwater. Lake sill elevation is estimated as being equal to the measured main-channel water level on the first day that floodwater was observed to have flooded into a lake. Since the exact time of lake flooding is not known, the lake sill elevation was estimated to equal the mean channel water level between the last observation of the lake being not flooded and the first observation of lake flooding.

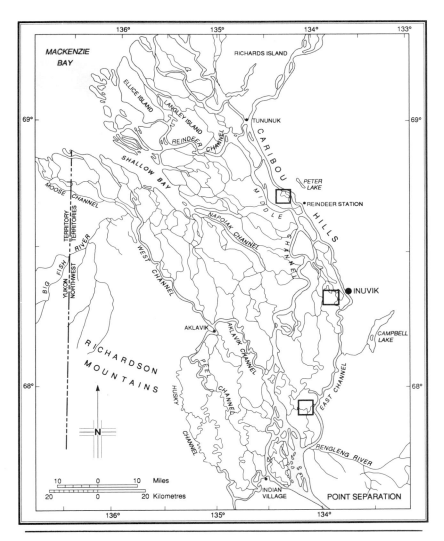

Figure 1. The Mackenzie Delta showing the three study areas (□): Gills Camp area in the northern portion of the Delta, the NRC Lake in the central Delta near Inuvik, and the Dishwater Lake area in the southern portion of the Delta.

Given the range of sill levels and the slow rate of rise of the main-channel water levels, surveys carried out at two-day intervals over a 20-day period provide estimates of sill level with an accuracy of approximately 0.5 m. Using this

Marsh and Hey

technique we have measured the spring sills of 165 lakes in the Dishwater area, 132 lakes in the NRC Lake area, and 199 lakes in the Gills Camp area.

In order to conduct a frequency analysis for extreme water-level events, main-channel water levels for the NRC Lake area were obtained from Brown (1957), the Inuvik Scientific Research Centre, and Water Survey of Canada records for East Channel at Inuvik. Records for spring peak level are available for 1954 and 1964 to the present. The Dishwater Lake and Gills Camp areas do not have records as long as those for the NRC Lake area, with only approximately 5 years of data for each site during the spring break-up. In order to extend the limited record for the Gills Camp and Dishwater Lake areas, we conducted a simple regression analysis between water levels at Inuvik and the other two sites.

RESULTS

Lake Sill Elevations

The measured sill elevations for each of the three study areas are shown in Figure 2 and summarized in Table 1. These changes in lake sill elevation show the following features as one moves southward from the low-lying outer Delta to the higher, upper Delta: (1) the mean sill level rises from 2.11 m a.s.l. at Gills Camp to 6.84 m a.s.l. at Dishwater Lake, (2) the shape of the sill elevation distribution curves changes from positively skewed at Gills Camp, to a near symmetrical distribution at both NRC Lake and Dishwater Lake sites, (3) the range of sill levels at a given site increases from only 2 m at Gills Camp to 4.5 m at Dishwater Lake, and as a result the number of lakes in the modal class decreases from over 35% to less than 20%.

These variations in sill levels may be explained, at least in a very general way, by lake-evolution processes. Lake formation in the outer Delta is dominated by the creation of lakes on coastal islands in estuarine mouths. These lakes

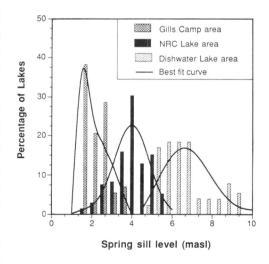

Figure 2. Measured spring sill elevations for the three study areas. Also shown is a best-fit curve for each data set.

Table 1. Variations in lake sill elevations and levee heights at the three study sites. Levee heights have been estimated from Mackay (1963) data for levee heights above low water. These values were then converted to m a.s.l. assuming that low water at Inuvik is 1.0 m a.s.l. (approximately the 5-year return period for low water levels, Marsh and Hey, 1989).

	CHANNEL DISTANCE (km)	MINIMUM SILL LEVEL (m a.s.l.)	MEAN SILL LEVEL (m a.s.l.)	MAXIMUM SILL LEVEL (m a.s.l.)	LEVEE HEIGHT (m a.s.l.)
Dishwater Lake area	0	5.0	6.84	9.5	11.9
NRC Lake area	59	1.5	3.92	5.5	8.0
Gills Camp area	119	1.5	2.11	3.5	4.0

are typically shallow, low-lying, and relatively large. With increasing distance from the delta front, lakes are gradually modified by a suite of processes. These include the growth of levees around lake perimeters, sedimentation within the lakes, delta cut-off processes, and accentuation of existing relief between permafrost and non-permafrost areas due to frost heave (Marsh, 1990). The overall result is to isolate lakes from the surrounding lake and channel systems, to divide large lakes into a number of smaller lakes, and to raise the general elevation of the lakes. If these processes continued unabated it would be expected that lakes in the upper Delta would be limited to a narrow elevation band. However, as shown in Figure 2, this is not the case. Instead, other processes continue to form new lakes at a range of sill levels. For example, channel abandonment and point-bar development lead to the formation of lakes with low sill elevations, while thermokarst processes tend to lead to the development of high sill-elevation lakes. The result is a wide range of lake sills in each of the three study areas.

In Figure 3, variations in lake sill elevations are compared to late-summer main-channel

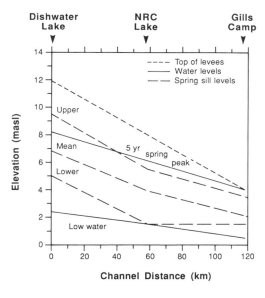

Figure 3. Variations in spring sill elevations, levee heights, and 5-year return period spring peak water levels, and typical late-summer low-water levels.

Marsh and Hey

water levels and changes in maximum levee heights at each study area. As described by Lewis (1988), levee heights have a steeper slope than the low water slope, so that the range between the two is approximately 10 m in the Dishwater Lake area, but only 4 m at Gills Camp. The upper band of lake sill elevations is approximately 3-m lower than the maximum levee height at both the Dishwater Lake and NRC Lake areas. At the Gills Camp area, however, maximum sill levels are only 2-m below maximum levees. The lower band of sill levels varies from approximately 2-m above typical low-water levels at Dishwater, to approximately equal to low water at both NRC and Gills Camp areas. However, it must be realized that due to the effect of snow and ice, sill levels measured in the spring are typically 0.5 to 1.5-m higher than summer sill levels. As a result, the spring sill levels discussed in this paper cannot be directly compared to summer water levels.

Spring Peak Water Levels and Lake Flooding

There is a good relationship between spring peak water levels at Gills Camp and those at East Channel at Inuvik (Figure 4) with an $r^2 = 0.86$. At Dishwater Lake, however, the relationship is not as good with an $r^2 = 0.63$. It is believed that the primary reason for this difference is that the Dishwater Lake water levels are greatly affected by the jamming of ice in East Channel downstream from the divergence of East Channel from Middle Channel. This jamming process varies greatly from year-to-year. Water levels at NRC and Gills Camp areas, however, are dominated by thermal break-ups, which do not vary greatly from year-to-year.

Using these relationships, the return period of spring peak water levels at both Gills Camp and Dishwater Lake areas can be estimated from the NRC Lake area data as shown in Figure 5. These data show that the annual (1-year return period)

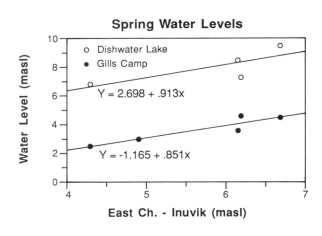

Figure 4. Relationship between spring peak water levels at East Channel at Inuvik and the Dishwater Lake and Gills Camp areas.

peak level varies from approximately 2.2 m a.s.l. at Gills Camp, to 4.2 m a.s.l. at NRC to 6.3 m a.s.l. at Dishwater Lake. Similarly, spring floods with a 5-year return period increase from 4.0 to 6.1 to 8.4 m a.s.l. at the three study sites.

Comparing these data to the lake sill elevations shows a large variation in the frequency of lake flooding. At the Gills Camp area, water levels with a 1-year return period flood 87% of lakes, while the 5-year peak level will flood all lakes in the area. Similarly, at the NRC area the 1-year peak level floods 67% of lakes, and again the 5-year peak level floods all lakes. Finally, at the Dishwater Lake area the 1-year peak level floods only 56% of lakes, while the 5-year peak level floods 87% of lakes. As shown in Figure 3, it appears that it is only in these southern parts of the

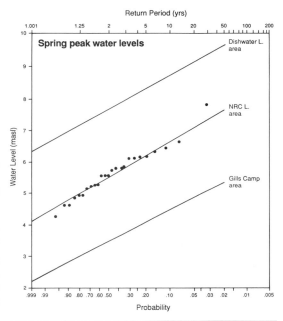

Figure 5. Return period of spring peak water levels for East Channel at Inuvik, plotted on Gumbel extreme-value probability paper. Solid dots represent measured data, while the line represents the Gumbel distribution fitted to the data. The lines for the Dishwater Lake and Gills Camp areas have been estimated using the relationships given in Figure 4.

delta that on average lake flooding is greater than 5 years, with the highest elevation lakes having flooding return periods in excess of 10 years. It should be realized, however, that given the very short data record for this area, and the limitations of extending the data record, this estimate of flood return period for the highest-elevation lakes must be viewed cautiously.

Marsh and Hey (1989) defined high-closure lakes as those lakes which have sill elevations greater than the 1-year return period of spring peak levels. In other words, these lakes are not flooded every spring. Using this definition, the number of high-closure lakes varies from 13%, to 33%, to 44% as you progress upwards through the Delta.

The frequency with which levees are overtopped can also be estimated from Figure 5 and the levee heights shown in Table 1. As expected, the frequency of

Marsh and Hey

levee overtopping decreases in an upstream direction, with a return period of approximately 4 years in the Gills Camp area, in excess of 50 years in the NRC Lake area, and in excess of 100 years in the Dishwater Lake area. For the Gills Camp and NRC Lake areas, these values seem reasonable. For the Dishwater Lake area our data record is far too short to allow us to have confidence in the above-mentioned value.

DISCUSSION

This analysis has shown that during the spring flood, most lakes in the eastern Delta are not flooded annually, but they are flooded every few years. The percentage of lakes which do not flood annually increases as you move up the Delta, and only in the Dishwater Lake area do some lakes have flood return periods in excess of 5 years.

Previous water-balance work (Marsh, 1986) has suggested that without flooding, delta lakes have a negative water balance, and as a result the lakes experience declining water levels between flooding events. Given that spring run-off from the surrounding basins is negligible (Marsh, 1990), that lake evaporation is greater than summer precipitation (Marsh and Bigras, 1988), and that mean lake depths are often between 1 and 1.5 m, delta lakes can survive only a few years without flooding. This is clearly demonstrated by the example of Dishwater Lake. This lake, which has a sill level in excess of 9 m a.s.l. and an estimated flood return period of over 10 years (Figure 5), was not flooded between 1982 and 1985. During this period water levels dropped by approximately 2.4 m. The water-level regime, and therefore the biological conditions of lakes like Dishwater Lake, are very different from the lower-elevation lakes which flood at intervals of less than 5 years. Lakes which flood infrequently experience large variations in water level, with levels declining to the point where the lake freezes to the bed in winter, or even dries up completely for short periods of time.

Delta lakes which are flooded less than annually are most sensitive to changes in the Mackenzie River regime. Small decreases in peak water levels, whether due to hydro development or climate change, would have serious impacts on lake regimes, with major consequences to the delta ecosystem.

REFERENCES

BIGRAS, S.C., 1990. Hydrological regime of lakes in the Mackenzie Delta, Northwest Territories, Canada. Arctic and Alpine Research, 22(2), 163-174

BROWN, R.J.E., 1957. Observations on break-up in the Mackenzie River and its delta in 1954. Journal of Glaciology, 3(22), 133-141

GILL, D., 1971. Vegetation and environment in the Mackenzie River Delta, N.W.T.: a study in subarctic ecology. Ph.D. thesis, Department of Geography, University of British Columbia, Vancouver, B.C., 694 pp.

HIRST, S.M., M. MILES, S.P. BLACHUT, L.A. GOULET and R.E. TAYLOR, 1987. Quantitative synthesis of the Mackenzie Delta ecosystems. Applied Ecology Ltd., North Vancouver, B.C. for Inland Waters Directorate, Western and Northern Region, Conservation and Protection, Environment Canada, Edmonton, Alberta, December, main volume, 407 pp.; appendices, 141 pp.

LEWIS, C.P., 1988. Mackenzie Delta sedimentary environments and processes. Draft Contract Report to Sediment Survey Section, Water Resources Branch, Inland Waters Directorate, Environment Canada, Ottawa, Ontario, January 26, 395 pp.

MACKAY, J.R., 1963. The Mackenzie Delta area, N.W.T. Geographical Branch Memoir No.8, Department of Mines and Technical Surveys, Ottawa, Ontario, 202 pp.

MARSH, P., 1986. Modelling water levels for a lake in the Mackenzie Delta. Proceedings of the Symposium: Cold Regions Hydrology, D.L. Kane (Editor), 22-25 July 1986, Fairbanks, Alaska, American Water Resources Association Technical Publication Series No.TPS-86-1, Bethesda, Maryland, 23-29

MARSH, P., 1990. Permafrost and lakes in the Mackenzie Delta. Permafrost - Canada, Proceedings of the 5th Canadian Permafrost Conference, 6-8 June 1990, Québec, Quebec, National Research Council Canada and Centre d'études nordiques, Collection Nordicana, No.54, 131-136

MARSH, P. and S.C. BIGRAS, 1988. Evaporation from Mackenzie Delta lakes, N.W.T., Canada. Arctic and Alpine Research, 20(2), 220-229

MARSH, P. and M. HEY, 1989. The flooding hydrology of Mackenzie Delta lakes near Inuvik, N.W.T., Canada. Arctic, 42(1), 41-49

Marsh and Hey

THE INFLUENCE OF FREQUENCY AND DURATION OF FLOODING ON THE NUTRIENT CHEMISTRY OF MACKENZIE DELTA LAKES*

L.F.W. Lesack[1]*, R.E. Hecky[2], and P. Marsh[1]

[1]National Hydrology Research Institute
11 Innovation Boulevard
Saskatoon, Saskatchewan
S7N 3H5   CANADA

[2]Department of Fisheries and Oceans
Freshwater Institute
501 University Crescent
Winnipeg, Manitoba
R3T 2N6   CANADA

*Present address:
Department of Geography
Simon Fraser University
Burnaby, British Columbia
V5A 1S6   CANADA

ABSTRACT

Among lakes associated with floodplains of the world's largest rivers, lakes in the Mackenzie River Delta are representative of a climatic extreme. Given low local precipitation, characteristic of the coastal arctic location, flooding is the dominant component in the water balance of the lakes, and balances are often negative in the absence of flooding. The length of time that a lake remains flooded with river water during a given year, the frequency of flooding between years, and the composition of nutrients and major solutes in the lake water is therefore expected to be related to the sill elevation of the lake. From ambient concentrations of C, N, P, and major ionic solutes in samples from 42 lakes of known sill elevation, we found that total ionic concentration is not directly related to sill elevations. A Q-mode factor model, however, which classifies the samples as mixtures of 3 independent ionic compositions (end-members), accounts for 98% of the variance in ionic composition among the sampled lakes. End-members 1 and 2 represent a system, shifting from relatively high Ca^{2+} with moderate HCO_3^- and SO_4^{2-} to a composition of moderate Mg^{2+} with high HCO_3^- and no SO_4^{2-}, which is strongly related to the sill elevations of the lakes. End-member 3 is an association of Na^+, Mg^{2+}, Cl^-, and SO_4^{2-} which is inversely related to ambient pH in the lakes. The highest and lowest concentrations of C and N among the lakes are associated with high relative pH, while intermediate concentrations are associated with the lowest pH values. These

*National Hydrology Research Institute Contribution Series Number CS-89078.

relations demonstrate the expected importance of flushing with river water and evaporation in determining the solute composition of the lakes, but also indicate an important role for biogeochemical processes occurring within the lakes.

INTRODUCTION

Studies of the hydrology and ecology of lakes in the Mackenzie Delta are justified from two independent perspectives which are complementary. First, economically because hydro-electric development on southern tributaries (the Liard, for example) seems inevitable. There is potential for oil spills from the future Mackenzie Valley pipeline and from present pumping stations on islands at Norman Wells. Moreover, given the northern location and the lengthy north-flowing drainage of the Mackenzie River, the Delta may be particularly susceptible to the effects of global climate change, either from changes in precipitation (upstream forcing) or from changes in sea level (downstream forcing). The second perspective, however, is that our understanding of the fundamental ecosystem processes operating in large rivers has remained very poor (Sedell *et al.*, 1989; Junk *et al.*, 1989). Much of our present understanding of riverine ecosystems is based on either low-order drainages of North America and Europe, or large tropical rivers that were studied prior to construction of reservoirs. The Mackenzie is one of the few relatively unmodified large rivers remaining in the world. It is also representative of a climatic extreme, being one of the largest rivers in the world which is ice-covered for a considerable portion of the year.

Large rivers cannot be experimentally manipulated. However, much can be learned from comparative studies with systems in other biomes, and conversely, more can be learned about other biomes by including another reference system in the analysis. The Mackenzie Delta receives near-desert amounts of local precipitation and previous work has established that lakes receive little run-off from their local drainage basins, while flooding by the Mackenzie dominates the water balance of the lakes (Marsh and Bigras, 1988; Marsh, 1986). With these characteristics, a given lake should always flood when the water level in the river overtops the elevation of the lake, and flooding should be more important in lower-elevation lakes, while less important in higher lakes. This does not necessarily have to be the case, as for example in rain-forest drainages, where local rainfall and run-off can be a sufficiently large component of lacustrine water balances to prevent flood water from entering lakes, even during periods of rising river level (Lesack, 1988).

Given these hydrological characteristics, Mackenzie Delta lakes are expected to represent a system where flooding is maximally important in controlling lacustrine nutrient inputs, among lakes associated with the floodplains of major world rivers. As part of more comprehensive studies of the hydrology and ecology of the Mackenzie Delta lakes, Marsh and Hey (1989) determined the annual frequency and duration with which flooding occurs in lakes in the central region of the Delta. From the water chemistry of 42 lakes located within their study area, we evaluate whether the ionic composition of the lakes can be predicted from the known flood frequency and duration, and we discuss the potential for biogeochemical processes within the lakes to also control water chemistry.

STUDY AREA AND METHODS

The Mackenzie Delta is a lake rich environment (*ca.* 25,000 lakes) located in the zone of continuous permafrost. The open-water period in the central Delta is from June to November, with peak water levels occurring during spring break-up in response to snowmelt run-off in more southerly parts of the Mackenzie basin. Secondary peaks occur during sporadic summer rains. Entry of river water into the delta lakes (flooding) is controlled by the elevation of the lakes relative to water levels in the river distributary channels (Marsh and Hey, 1989). On average, spring flooding commences during mid-May, with the mean peak water level of 5.6 m a.s.l. occurring in East Channel at Inuvik on June 3. After this date, the lake levels fall rapidly in response to falling Mackenzie River levels, with water levels dropping an average of 1.04 m (or 58% of the flood peak) over a 4-day period following the peak.

In lakes of sufficiently high elevation, flooding does not occur during the summer and the only water input during summer is rainfall directly onto their surface. Annual precipitation averages only 266 mm at Inuvik, of which approximately 57% occurs as snow. Since ground-water flow from these lakes is restricted by permafrost beneath the land portion of the basin (Johnston and Brown, 1964, 1966) and the unfrozen, low-permeability sediments beneath the lakes (Marsh, 1990), loss of water during summer is dominated by evaporation. Since open-water evaporation is typically greater than precipitation within the delta (Marsh and Bigras, 1988), water levels in lakes isolated from the river channels slowly decline through the summer until freeze-up in early-October.

Frequency and Duration of Flooding

Since the flooding of Mackenzie Delta lakes is controlled by the elevation of the lakes relative to water levels in the river, Marsh and Hey (1989) operationally defined "sill elevation" as the highest elevation along the connecting channel thalweg between the lake and river channel. To quantify the frequency and duration with which lakes are flooded, Marsh and Hey determined the sill elevations for a set of 132 lakes in the central Delta (Figure 1). Comparing the sill elevations of these lakes to the long-term water-level record (25 years) for East Channel at Inuvik (Marsh and Hey, 1989), subsequently established that 2/3 of the lakes are flooded annually in the spring, the remaining 1/3 flood with a frequency of between 1 and 4 years, and water levels fall to sufficiently low levels by late-summer to isolate 88% of the lakes from the river.

These results provided operational quantification of a simple lake classification system proposed by Mackay (1963). No-closure lakes remain in connection with

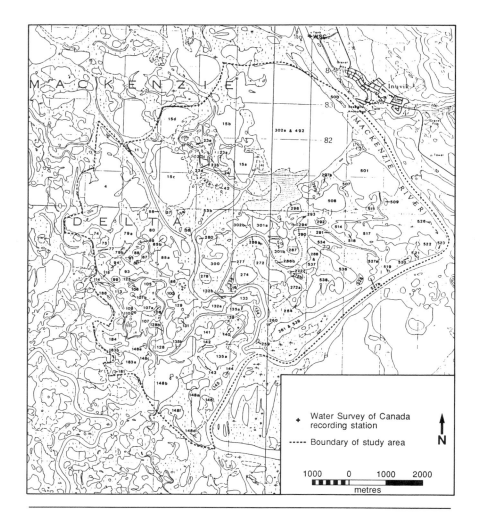

Figure 1. Map of the study area.

main channels for the entire summer and are defined as lakes with sill elevations lower than the one-year return period for summer low water levels in the river. Low-closure lakes are flooded each spring but are cut off from the river for some portion of the summer, and are defined by sill elevations higher than no-closure lakes but less than the one-year return period for spring peak water levels in the river. High-closure lakes are not flooded every spring and never during the summer, and are defined by sill elevations greater than the one-year return period for spring peak water levels. The three classes of lakes respectively represent 12%, 55%, and 33% of the lakes within the study area (Marsh and Hey, 1989).

To evaluate the variation in water chemistry as a function of flood frequency, a sub-set of 42 lakes with known sill elevation was selected (from the 132) and sampled during late summer of 1987, when the flooding effects from the previous spring could be considered finished.

Collection and Analysis of Water Samples

Water samples were collected in clean plastic bottles and were usually shipped within a day to the analytical laboratory at the Freshwater Institute in Winnipeg for subsequent analysis. Sample filtrations, subsampling, measurement of pH, and acid titrations were performed promptly upon arrival in Winnipeg (usually within 2 to 3 days of collection), and thereafter samples were kept refrigerated until analyzed. pH and acid titrations were performed on aliquots of unfiltered water, while measurements for major solutes were performed on aliquots of water filtered through rinsed Whatman GF/C glass fibre filters and a plastic filtration apparatus. Cations (Na^+, K^+, Ca^{2+}, Mg^{2+}) were measured by atomic absorption spectrophotometry, and anions (Cl^-, SO_4^{2-}) by Dionex ion chromatography. Dissolved inorganic carbon (DIC) was determined from Gran's plot analysis (Gran, 1950, 1952) of acid titration curves and for subsequent data analyses was assumed to be in the form of HCO_3^-. Given that the pH of the samples ranged as high as 8.7, there could have been significant amounts of CO_3^{2-} in some of the samples. *In situ* pHs measured in the field at mid-day (not reported in this paper) are significantly higher than pH's reported by the lab (Anema *et al.*, 1990a, 1990b), and indicate that appreciable depletion of DIC concentrations may have occurred in ambient lake water as a result of photosynthesis.

The total dissolved fractions of nitrogen (TDN) and phosphorus (TDP) were measured, from filtered aliquots of sample, by digestion techniques with subsequent measurement of the inorganic forms of nitrogen and phosphorus. The particulate fractions (PN and PP) were measured by digesting the material collected on the filter with subsequent measurement of inorganic nitrogen and phosphorus in the extract. Dissolved organic carbon (DOC) was measured from filtered aliquots of sample. Further details of analytical methods and sample treatment protocols are given in Stainton *et al.* (1977). Further details of sample collection and processing are given in Anema *et al.* (1990a, 1990b).

In situ profiles of conductivity and temperature were measured with a Yellow Springs Instruments Model 33 SCT meter, with a conductivity cell constant of 1.0. Temperatures were derived from a thermistor bead probe, readable to 0.1°C, and calibrated against a certified thermometer.

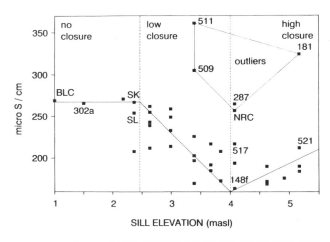

Figure 2. Conductivity of ambient lake water versus sill elevation of the lake. No-closure, low-closure, and high-closure ranges of sill elevation correspond to Marsh and Hey's (1989) modification of Mackay's (1963) lake classification system. Trend lines were fit by eye. Lake numbers associated with data points correspond to the numbering in Figure 1. Abbreviations are: BLC (Big Lake Channel), SK (Skidoo Lake; 85 on map), SL (South Lake; 129 on map), NRC (NRC Lake; 278 on map).

The relation between the conductivity of ambient lake water and the sill elevation of the lake seems to be different within the ranges of sill elevation that correspond to Mackay's three classes of lakes (Figure 2). Conductivities within the no-closure lakes, increasing in sill elevation from "Big Lake Channel" to "Skidoo Lake", are relatively invariant. All of these lakes were connected to the river channels at the time of sampling. Conductivities decrease within the range of low-closure lakes, as elevations increase from Skidoo Lake to Lake 148f. Within the range of high-closure lakes, conductivities subsequently appear to increase as elevations increase from Lake 148f to Lake 521. This relation, however, would not be discernible if Lake 521 was removed from the plot. There is also a cluster of outliers, with relatively high sill elevations, that include Lakes 181, 511, 509, 287, and "NRC". The conductivities of these outliers cannot be reconciled as a simple function of lake size since three of the lakes are small while two are of moderate size (Figure 1).

Q-Mode Factor Model

To determine if the chemistry of the lakes could be classified in some simple manner, Q-mode factor analysis was performed (Jöreskog *et al.*, 1976; Davis, 1986). Factor analysis is most commonly based on an R-mode model where the objective is to partition a set of variables which are inter-correlated across a set of samples into uncorrelated combinations of related variables only. The model for Q-mode analysis is mathematically analogous to the R-mode model. However, the Q-mode model is a sample classification technique where, given a data matrix of N rows representing samples and p columns representing variables measured on each sample, the goal is to account for the inter-relations between each pair of samples in the set (N by N comparisons), rather than describe the covariation among the variables (p by p comparisons). Instead of correlation co-efficients, which describe covariation between pairs of variables, the analysis is based on an index that measures the proportional similarity between any given pair of samples in the set of data. The most common index is the cosine of the angle between the two given row vectors (samples) defined by their respective co-ordinates in p dimensional space (Imbrie and Purdy, 1962), which for any two samples (n) and (m) is calculated as:

$$[1] \qquad \cos\theta_{nm} = \frac{\left[\sum_{j=1}^{p} x_{nj} \cdot x_{mj} \right]}{\left[\sum_{j=1}^{p} x_{nj}^2 \cdot \sum_{j=1}^{p} x_{mj}^2 \right]^{1/2}}$$

Since this is a measure of relative composition, the raw data are not transformed to logarithms, as may be necessary for R-mode analysis.

In matrix notation drawn from Jöreskog *et al.* (1976), the N by N matrix of similarities ($\cos\theta$ values) is defined as:

$$[2] \qquad Q = W \cdot W'$$

where W is the row-normalized matrix derived from the matrix X of raw data and is calculated as:

$$[3] \qquad W = D^{-1/2} \cdot X$$

and where D is an N by N diagonal matrix of the row sum of squares of X.

The row normalized data matrix is related to the basic factor model as:

$$[4] \qquad W = A \cdot F' + E$$

where A is an N by k matrix of factor loadings, F is a p by k matrix of factor scores, E is an N by p matrix of residual errors, and k is the number of factors (k < p) postulated for the model. Translated into scalar notation, the value of the i*th* variable in a given sample is:

$$[5] \qquad w_i = \sum_{j=1}^{k} a_j \cdot f_{ij} + e_i$$

where a_j represents the elements of the appropriate row (corresponding to the given sample) of matrix A, f_{ij} represents the elements of matrix F, and e_i represents the i*th* element from the appropriate row of matrix E. This equation states that each observed variable w_i is a weighted sum of factors plus a residual error term.

Assuming orthogonality of the factors, the relation between the known N by N matrix of similarities and the factor model reduces to:

[6] $Q = A \cdot A' + \epsilon$

where ϵ is an N by N diagonal matrix of residual errors. For a given combination of A and ϵ that satisfy Equation 6, however, the estimate of A is not unique. Postmultiplication of matrix A by any k by k orthogonal matrix T will rigidly rotate the vectors of A to new positions without affecting the estimates of communalities or residual error, and yields a new matrix A_T that also satisfies Equation 6. This indeterminacy is typically utilized to rotate the factors to more meaningful positions relative to the original co-ordinate system. The Q-mode factor solution attempts to reconcile the relative composition of each sample in the data set as a mixture of several end-member compositions. The number of factors required for an acceptable rotated solution represents the number of independent end-members. The factor scores represent the composition of the end-members relative to average composition, while the factor loading co-efficients represent the relative amount of each end-member in each of the samples.

The objective of rotation is to arrange the factors so that each contains only a few highly-loaded samples and many insignificant loadings. The Varimax method of Kaiser (1958), the most common of the various rotation methods, attempts to satisfy the above objective by maximizing the variances of the factor loadings on each factor, under the constraint that the factors remain orthogonal. The matrix of factor loadings after Varimax rotation is thus defined as:

[7] $A_{vx} = A \cdot T_{vx}$

where T_{vx} is a k by k transformation matrix that satisfies Equation 7 according to the Varimax criteria. After rotation of the loadings, the corresponding rotated factor scores are obtained by postmultiplication of the factor score matrix F by T_{vx}.

A second indeterminacy in the analysis is to objectively select the number of factors to be extracted. A variety of criteria have been suggested of which none are acclaimed to be uniquely correct. Jöreskog *et al.* (1976) recommend extracting as many as necessary to account for 95 to 99% of the variance, then orthogonal rotation of the factors by an objective procedure, such as Varimax, to determine if any of the factors persistently retain a trivial amount of information. If a factor contributes minimal information to the rotated solution, the last unrotated factor is deleted and the rotation repeated. This iteration procedure is repeated until no trivial factors remain, but is stopped before the factor solution is distorted by retaining too few factors. A strong critique of the indeterminacies in factor analysis is given by Temple (1978).

Ionic Composition of the End-Member Samples

Three factors accounted for more than 99% of the variance in the data and seemed to be the appropriate solution for the factor model. Comparison of the Eigen values and variance accounted for by successive factors, extracted before rotation, show that the information content among the factors was redistributed into three near-equal portions by the Varimax rotation (Table 1). The Varimax factor scores, which represent the relative composition of each factor (end-member) are shown in Table 1. An advantage of Q-mode factor analysis is that the actual samples which load most heavily on a given end-member can be identified from the loading co-efficients, and the composition of the samples that most closely approximate the end-members can be directly inspected and compared. The samples which most closely approximate end-members are respectively from Lakes 302a, 521, and 517. Their ionic compositions are shown in Figure 3. Lake 302a (end-member 1) is in the lowest sill-elevation band among the lakes and has a loading co-efficient similar to Big Lake Channel. The factor scores indicate a signal of higher than average Ca^{2+} with moderate HCO_3^- and SO_4^{2-}. Lake 521 (end-member 2) is in the highest sill-elevation band, and is also the endpoint in the relation between conductivity and sill elevation among the high-closure lakes (Figure 2). The factor scores indicate a signal of moderate Mg^{2+} with high HCO_3^- and little SO_4^{2-}. Lake 517 (end-member 3) has a sill elevation approximately equal to the elevation which separates the lakes which flood every year (low-closure) from those which do not (high-closure). The factor scores indicate a signal of higher than average Na^+, Mg^{2+}, Cl^-, and SO_4^{2-}.

A simultaneous plot of the fractional content of end-members 1 and 2 in each sample vs sill elevation (Figure 4; Loading co-efficients were converted to fractional content as a_j^2 from Equation 5) shows a relatively strong reciprocal relation with increasing sill elevation. A plot of end-member 3 content vs sill elevation (Figure 5A) indicates there is no direct relation, but has a

Table 1. Varimax factor scores obtained for the Q-mode factor model.

VARIABLE	FACTOR 1	FACTOR 2	FACTOR 3
Na^+	-0.176	0.124	0.401
K^+	0.003	0.016	-0.002
Ca^{2+}	0.821	-0.121	0.121
Mg^{2+}	-0.244	0.405	0.537
Cl^-	-0.146	0.110	0.277
SO_4^{2-}	0.201	-0.437	0.678
HCO_3^-	0.417	0.776	0.016
Information Content of the Factor Loadings:			
(%)	37.7	33.7	28.4
Before Varimax Rotation:			
Eigen values	40.9	0.63	0.43
Cumulative Variance (%)	97.3	98.8	99.8

Lesack et al.

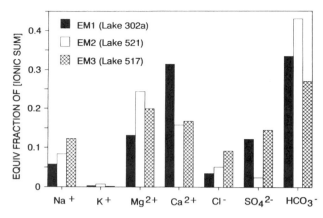

Figure 3. Ionic composition of the water samples from the lakes which most closely approximate end-member compositions (EM1-EM3). Ionic composition is expressed as the relative fraction (in equivalents) of the sum of ionic solutes.

wave-form shape. A plot of end-member 3 content vs pH (Figure 5B), however, shows a relatively strong relation.

Indices of Productivity in the Lakes

To obtain a rough sense of how productive the lakes might be and whether productivity might be related to pH, plots of C, N, and P were examined. DOC on average represents 84% of TOC in the samples, and TDN represents 96% of TN. The relation between DOC and TDN vs sill elevation (Figure 6) shows a rough trend of increasing concentrations as elevations increase. TDP represents only 48% of TP in the samples, and is unrelated to sill elevation.

The relation between DOC and pH (Figure 7) is double banded with end points at Big Lake Channel, Lake 181, and roughly intersecting at Lakes 517 and 111. The relation between TDN and pH (Figure 7) is also double banded, and appears to be even tighter than for DOC. Since the sill elevations of Lakes 517 and 111 respectively are 4.1 and 3.7 m a.s.l., which corresponds to the transition between low-closure and high-closure lakes, it appears that there is a pH-related change in chemistry as the lakes are flooded less frequently and for shorter duration. Since high-closure lakes are isolated from flushing shortly after the spring flood, changes in chemistry could be caused by evaporative concentration, within-lake geochemical processes, or perhaps by thermokarst processes. Because changes in chemistry are associated with high concentrations of organic C and N, however, the implication is that the changes are related to the biota of the lakes. We emphasize that almost all of these lakes were flooded in this year, and would not be surprised if other differences were present during years with lower peak water levels when all of the lakes would not be flooded.

DISCUSSION

There are a complex variety of within-lake processes, both biotic and abiotic, that can effect the chemistry of lakes in the Mackenzie Delta. Based on work in progress, the following are processes which could potentially be important.

Biotic Processes

There is a strong gradient of light penetration among the lakes (Fee *et al.*, 1988) which is a function of flood frequency and duration. Low sill-elevation lakes that continue to exchange water with the river channel throughout the summer are the most turbid, while high sill-elevation lakes which are only flooded during the spring for relatively brief duration become quite transparent during the summer. In the higher-elevation lakes, a

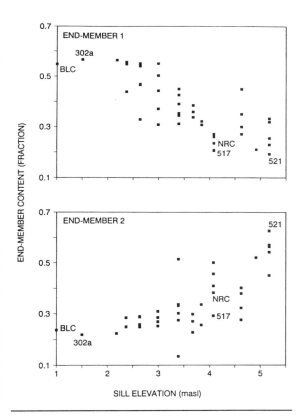

Figure 4. Plots of the content of end-members 1 and 2 in the samples of lake water versus sill elevation of the lake. End-member content is derived as a_j^2 from the loading co-efficient in Equation 5.

relatively dense growth of aquatic macrophytes typically develops, usually dominated by *Potamogeton sp.*, after the decline of spring water levels. Hecky *et al.* (1991) have demonstrated that the availability of light strongly controls algal and submerged macrophyte photosynthesis. In four delta lakes ranging from turbid to relatively transparent, phytoplankton areal photosynthetic rates varied less than two fold, while areal macrophyte net photosynthesis varied by more than a factor of 20 and accounted for more than 95% of community photosynthesis in the clearest lake (NRC Lake).

In productive lakes there can be strong interaction between pH, DIC, and Ca^{2+} which is driven by photosynthesis. During periods of high photosynthetic rates,

Lesack et al.

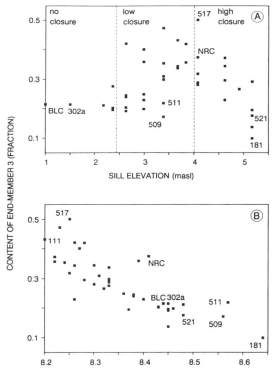

uptake and subsequent depletion of the free CO_2, which is required to maintain the stability of Ca^{2+} and HCO_3^- in solution can result in high pHs (>9) and precipitation of $CaCO_3$ until equilibrium is re-established. In NRC Lake, *in situ* pHs greater than 10 and precipitation of $CaCO_3$ have been frequently observed during periods of high macrophyte growth (Anema *et al.*, 1990a, 1990b). Given that Ca^{2+} and HCO_3^- are the two largest components of the ionic composition in the river water which floods these lakes, and are the dominant theoretical contributors to the conductivity of the water, there is large potential for macrophyte production to have a major impact on lake-water chemistry. Moreover, this provides a plausible explanation for why pH is related to end-member 3 of our factor model and is a useful measurement for water-chemistry classification of the delta lakes.

Figure 5. Plots of the content of end-member 3 versus each of sill elevation (A) and pH of the lake water (B).

Abiotic Processes

We have evidence that evaporation could be important in water balances and as a potential control on biogeochemical processes in these lakes. From the analysis of Marsh and Hey (1989), it is apparent that about 1/3 of the lakes do not flood every year. "Dishwater Lake", although not in our study area, is one particular example which had not been flooded since 1982 and steadily declined from evaporation (Marsh and Bigras, 1988) until it was flooded in 1988. The ionic composition of Dishwater Lake is dominated by a strong signal of Ca^{2+} and SO_4^{2-}, which is considerably different than can be reconciled by the end-member compositions determined from the factor model in our present analysis (Figure 3). Moreover, despite progressive evaporation of the lake over several years, the shift in ionic composition relative to river water seems to reflect that other biogeochemical processes have had greater effect than evaporative concentration *per se*.

Although the dominance of flooding in the water budget, in even relatively high elevation lakes such as NRC, seems plainly apparent, the role of flooding in preliminary nutrient- and solute-balance calculations is not completely clear. We have evidence that an unusual role can be played by the ice cover in these lakes. Despite cold arctic temperatures, and that the lakes are very shallow (mean depths less than 2 m), a layer of water commonly remains unfrozen beneath the ice cover and solute exclusion during growth of the ice can increase solute concentrations within the unfrozen water by several fold. The timing of peak

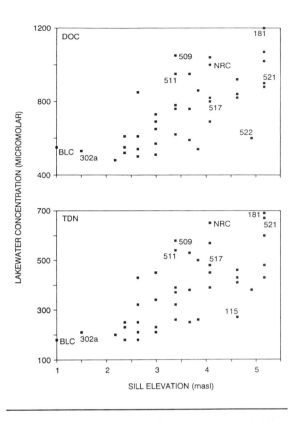

Figure 6. Plots of dissolved organic carbon (DOC) and total dissolved nitrogen (TDN) concentrations of the lake water samples versus sill elevation of the lake.

river levels during the spring is such that many lakes are flooded over the top of their ice cover. The ice pan eventually either fractures or releases from the lake bed and floats to the surface. At NRC Lake, profiles of temperature and water density derived from water-chemistry measurements taken during the 1989 flooding period indicate that little apparent mixing occurred between the flood water and the denser layer of unfrozen lake water (Lesack *et al.*, 1991). In this particular instance, the flood water apparently melted the ice cover, mixed with the ice-derived water, and drained from the lake while leaving the solutes from the previous year, within the layer of bottom water, behind. Hence, the spring flood is potentially able to provide a mechanism to trap and accumulate solutes within the lake, rather than flushing and initializing the lake with river water. How common this process might be among the delta lakes and the importance of a floating ice cover in shielding the lakes from

Lesack et al.

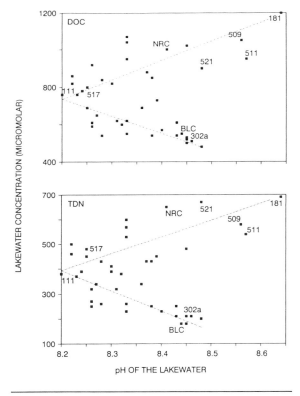

Figure 7. Plots of dissolved organic carbon (DOC) and total dissolved nitrogen (TDN) concentrations of the lake water samples versus pH of the lake water. Trend lines were fit by eye.

wind are being evaluated in continuing investigations.

A second observation from NRC Lake which casts uncertainty on the role of the flood in the solute and nutrient balance of the lakes is that during the 1989 period of flooding, the solute concentrations in the lake water (inferred from conductivity values) were always higher than in the adjacent river water. The range of conductivities that were recorded for the various sources of water contributed to the lake during this period, including a reference value for upland snowmelt run-off, are summarized in Table 2. Two types of local run-off can be distinguished for delta lakes (lowland) as opposed to upland areas adjacent to the Delta which are never flooded. Operationally, we have defined lowland snowmelt run-off as that derived from melting of the winter snowpack, and lowland postflood run-off as that derived from drainage of flood water from the landscape as the water levels of the spring flood recede. It is clear that both types of lowland run-off are substantially different from one another and from the upland snowmelt. Assuming that the two layers of lake water do not mix, however, the only source of water of sufficiently-high conductivity to increase the value of the mixed layer significantly above the value of the river water, is the postflood run-off. This preliminary evaluation suggests that there may be sufficient leaching from the flooded forest to be important in the solute balance of the lake. Budgetary calculations based on individual solutes, rather than conductivity, are being performed in continuing investigations to more rigorously evaluate the importance of the various sources of solutes.

Reconciliation of Conductivity and Sill Elevation of the Lakes

Based on the above observations it is possible to propose a potential reconciliation of the relation between conductivity and sill elevation of the lakes shown in Figure 2. The duration of the initial spring flood ranges from 5 to 120 days. From the values in Table 2 it is apparent that the lowest conductivity lakes are in the range of the river during the period of flooding (100-184 μS·cm^{-1}). The conductivity of the low-closure and no-closure lakes, which are flooded more frequently and for progressively longer duration through the summer, appear to track the increase in conductivity of river water over the summer. The conductivity of the high-closure lakes, which are only briefly flooded or not flooded at all, are higher presumably because of evaporative concentration. The cluster of outliers could potentially be lakes which have accumulated solutes by a combination of solute exclusion during growth of their ice cover and incomplete flushing during the subsequent period of flooding.

Table 2. Range of conductivities recorded for different sources of water contributed to NRC Lake during the 1989 period of flooding.

WATER SOURCES	μS·cm^{-1}
RIVER	100 - 184
LOCAL RUN-OFF	
Lowland Snowmelt	98 - 113
Lowland Postflood	325 - 427
[Upland Snowmelt]	22 - 45
LAKE WATER	
Mixed Layer	180 - 278
Bottom Layer	670 - 720

CONCLUSIONS

Returning to our original premise, we expected that given their hydrological characteristics, Mackenzie Delta lakes would represent a system where flooding is maximally important in controlling lacustrine nutrient inputs, among lakes associated with the floodplains of major world rivers. Some aspects of this are supported, but surprisingly some are not. The ionic composition of water in the lakes was related to the lake sill elevation and thereby supports an expected importance of flooding as one primary control on nutrient chemistry. However, there is also large potential for biogeochemical processes within the lakes to alter the lake water to a composition which is substantially different than the original sources.

Important biogeochemical processes include a potentially large role for aquatic macrophytes and flooded forest in mining nutrients from the deltaic sediments and making them available to the aquatic ecosystem through leaching and decomposition. Hence, despite the fact that the Delta is a depositional structure over the long-term average, it is apparently capable of acting as a source of nutrients on shorter time scales, which are more relevant to aquatic biota and humans. Given that some lakes can become isolated for considerable periods, evaporative concentration, microbial, and geochemical alteration of the ionic composition can be important. There is an unusual role for flooding in lakes of relatively high sill elevation, where the combination of brief flooding duration and solute-exclusion processes, provides a

Lesack et al.

potential mechanism for trapping solutes in the lakes, rather than flushing and initializing them with river water. Thermokarst effects from localized melting of ground ice are probably important, but at present are unknown.

A logical implication of our findings is that climate-induced changes in the lacustrine ecosystems in the Mackenzie Delta would be more difficult to predict than changes in water balance. If the hydrology of the delta becomes sufficiently well understood that it is possible to predict the water-level changes expected to occur with changes in global climate, there is temptation to conclude that the sustainability or demise of certain lakes in the delta could be predicted directly from their sill elevation. Our findings imply that complex changes could occur from relatively subtle changes in water level, and the changes will require considerably more work to predict.

ACKNOWLEDGEMENTS

We appreciate the assistance provided by Mary Ferguson and Cory Anema, and the laboratory measurements performed by the analytical unit of the Freshwater Institute. We acknowledge generous logistical support from the Polar Continental Shelf Project, Department of Energy, Mines, and Resources, and the Inuvik Scientific Resource Centre, Department of Indian and Northern Affairs. Financial support was received from the Northern Oil and Gas Action Program (NOGAP) through the Department of Fisheries and Oceans.

REFERENCES

ANEMA, C., R.E. HECKY, E.J. FEE, D. NERNBERG and S.J. GUILDFORD, 1990a. Water chemistry of some lakes and channels in the Mackenzie Delta and on the Tuktoyaktuk Peninsula, N.W.T., 1985. Canadian Data Report on Fisheries and Aquatic Sciences No.726, Fisheries and Oceans Canada, 80 pp.

ANEMA C., R.E. HECKY, S. HIMMER and S.J. GUILDFORD, 1990b. Water chemistry of some lakes and channels in the Mackenzie Delta and on the Tuktoyaktuk Peninsula, N.W.T., 1986. Canadian Data Report on Fisheries and Aquatic Sciences No.729, Fisheries and Oceans Canada, 63 pp.

DAVIS, J.C., 1986. Statistics and data analysis in geology. 2nd edition, John Wiley and Sons, Toronto, Ontario, 646 pp.

FEE, E.J., R.E. HECKY, S.J. GUILDFORD, C. ANEMA, D. MATHEW and K. HALLARD, 1988. Phytoplankton primary production and related limnological data for lakes and channels in the Mackenzie Delta and lakes on the Tuktoyaktuk Peninsula, N.W.T. Canadian Technical Report of Fisheries and Aquatic Sciences No.1614, Fisheries and Oceans Canada, 62 pp.

GRAN, G., 1950. Determination of the equivalent point in potentiometric titrations. Acta Chemica Scandinavica, 4(1), 559-577

GRAN, G., 1952. Determination of the equivalent point in potentiometric titrations: Part 2. The Analyst, Vol.77, 661-671

HECKY, R.E., R.H. HESSLEIN and P.S. RAMLAL, 1991. Net community photosynthesis in Mackenzie Delta lakes near Inuvik, N.W.T. In - Mackenzie Delta: Environmental Interactions and Implications of Development, P. Marsh and C.S.L. Ommanney (Editors), Proceedings of the Workshop on the Mackenzie Delta, 17-18 October 1989, Saskatoon, Saskatchewan, NHRI Symposium No.4, National Hydrology Research Institute, Environment Canada, Saskatoon, Saskatchewan, abstract, 69

IMBRIE, J. and E.G. PURDY, 1962. Classification of modern Bahamian carbonate sediments. In - Classification of Carbonate Rocks: a Symposium, W.E. Ham (Editor), 27 April 1961, Denver, Colorado, American Association of Petroleum Geologists Memoir No.1, 253-272

JOHNSTON, G.H. and R.J.E. BROWN, 1964. Some observations on permafrost distribution at a lake in the Mackenzie Delta, N.W.T., Canada. Arctic, 17(3), 163-175

JOHNSTON, G.H. and R.J.E. BROWN, 1966. Occurrence of permafrost at an arctic lake. Nature, 211(5052), 952-953

JÖRESKOG, K.G., J.E. KLOVAN and R.A. REYMENT, 1976. Geological factor analysis. Methods in Geomathematics I, Elsevier Scientific Publishing Co., New York, 178 pp.

JUNK, W.J., P.B. BAYLEY and R.E. SPARKS, 1989. The flood pulse concept in river-floodplain systems. In - Proceedings of the International Large River Symposium (LARS), D.P. Dodge (Editor), Canadian Special Publication of Fisheries and Aquatic Sciences No.106, Fisheries and Oceans Canada, 110-127

KAISER, H.F., 1958. The varimax criterion for analytic rotation in factor analysis. Psychometrika, 23(3), 187-200

LESACK, L.F.W., 1988. Mass balance of nutrients, major solutes, and water in an Amazon floodplain lake and biogeochemical implications for the Amazon Basin. Ph.D. Dissertation, University of California, Santa Barbara, California, 524 pp.

LESACK, L.F.W., P. MARSH and R.E. HECKY, 1991. Ice cover growth and freeze-out of solutes in a Mackenzie Delta lake. Proceedings, Northern Hydrology Symposium, T.D. Prowse and C.S.L. Ommanney (Editors), NHRI Symposium No.6, National Hydrology Research Institute, Environment Canada, Saskatoon, Saskatchewan, 219-236

MACKAY, J.R., 1963. The Mackenzie Delta area, N.W.T. Geographical Branch Memoir No.8, Department of Mines and Technical Surveys, Ottawa, Ontario, 202 pp.

MARSH, P., 1986. Modelling water levels for a lake in the Mackenzie Delta. Proceedings of the Symposium: Cold Regions Hydrology, D.L. Kane (Editor), 22-25 July 1986, Fairbanks, Alaska, American Water Resources Association Technical Publication Series No.TPS-86-1, Bethesda, Maryland, 23-29

MARSH, P., 1990. Permafrost and lakes in the Mackenzie Delta. Permafrost - Canada, Proceedings of the 5th Canadian Permafrost Conference, 6-8 June 1990, Québec, Quebec, National Research Council Canada and Centre d'études nordiques, Collection Nordicana, No.54, 131-136

MARSH, P. and S.C. BIGRAS, 1988. Evaporation from Mackenzie Delta lakes, N.W.T., Canada. Arctic and Alpine Research, 20(2), 220-229

MARSH, P. and M. HEY, 1989. The flooding hydrology of Mackenzie Delta lakes near Inuvik, N.W.T., Canada. Arctic, 42(1), 41-49

SEDELL, J.R., J.E. RICHEY and F.J. SWANSON, 1989. The river continuum concept: A basis for the expected behavior of very large rivers? In - Proceedings of the International Large River Symposium (LARS), D.P. Dodge (Editor), Canadian Special Publication of Fisheries and Aquatic Sciences No.106, Fisheries and Oceans Canada, 49-55

STAINTON, M.P., M.J. CAPEL and F.A.J. ARMSTRONG, 1977. The chemical analysis of freshwater. Miscellaneous Special Publication No.25, Fisheries and Marine Service, Fisheries and Environment Canada, 2nd edition, Freshwater Institute, Winnipeg, Manitoba, 180 pp.

TEMPLE, J.T., 1978. The use of factor analysis in geology. Journal of the International Association of Mathematical Geology, 10(4), 379-387

SEDIMENTATION IN THE MACKENZIE DELTA

P. Lewis

1212 Duke Street
Victoria, British Columbia
V8P 2B6   CANADA

ABSTRACT

The subaerial Mackenzie Delta has a surface area of 12,995 km² and is fronted by a 6,930 km² subaqueous delta front zone extending out to 12-m water depth. As such it is the second largest delta in North America to the Mississippi and the second largest arctic/subarctic delta in the world to the Lena River Delta in the U.S.S.R. The presently active "modern" delta occupies a river-eroded and glacier-modified structural trough and has formed largely during the past 12,000 years.

At the most general level, the subaerial Delta can be divided into upper and lower plains. The upper plain lies south of the limit of trees and is characterized by a complex system of intertwined channels, large numbers of delta lakes, levees and low alluvial flats and by the dominance of river processes. The lower plain lies within the zone of tidal influence and storm-surge flooding from the Beaufort Sea and is dominated by broad treeless flats with fewer larger lakes but numerous tiny ponds. The abruptly lower elevations on the lower plain appear to be the result of a marked increase in total distributary channel width. The dominance of lakes rather than marshes in interdistributary areas, on the other hand, may relate to a pronounced increase in the relative importance of organic accumulation on deltas in cold climatic zones.

The thickness of modern Mackenzie Delta sediments is only of the order of 60 to 90 m, but even this represents a total deposit volume of 1,200 km³. At the delta surface, sand dominates on point bars and along Middle Channel, but elsewhere, on levees and flats and in lakes and small channels, silt and clay normally prevail. These fine-grained sediments have low cohesion and little tendency to swell on wetting. Except beneath channels and lakes, the sediment is perennially frozen. Excess ice does exist, especially in the top 10 m, but not nearly to the same extent as in the bordering Pleistocene uplands. Measured bulk densities suggest that settlement on thawing would probably be less than 10 percent in many areas but, locally, potential settlement of 30 percent or more is possible.

The Mackenzie and Peel Rivers together have a mean annual water discharge of almost 10,000 m³·s⁻¹ and deliver in the order of 125-million metric tonnes of clayey silt with lesser sand to the Delta annually. This, in combination with the low wave-energy levels of the microtidal Beaufort Sea, suggests that the Mackenzie's morphology or form should be primarily river-controlled. This control is verified to

---

some extent by the very low offshore gradient which the Mackenzie has been able to maintain off its delta front. It is contradicted, however, by the ongoing erosion and retreat along the delta shoreline, retreat that averages over 2 m per year across the delta front. The answer appears to lie in marine transgression: the Mackenzie Delta is being inundated because of a relatively-rapid and continuing increase in relative sea levels at the delta front. In this situation, a delta surface can continue to aggrade as the Mackenzie's is, even in the face of shoreline recession.

SEDIMENT TRANSPORT AT THE MACKENZIE DELTA-BEAUFORT SEA INTERFACE

K.A. Jenner[1]* and P.R. Hill[2]

[1]Department of Geology
Dalhousie University
Halifax, Nova Scotia
B3H 3J5   CANADA

[2]Hill Geoscience Research
Small Business Technology Centre
70 Neptune Crescent
Dartmouth, Nova Scotia
B2Y 4M9   CANADA

*Present address:
 Deltamarine Consulting
 13 Elizabeth Street
 Dartmouth, Nova Scotia
 B2W 2T4   CANADA

ABSTRACT

The modern Mackenzie Delta is presently retreating at a rate of several metres per year in response to rising relative sea level. Nevertheless sedimentation continues in many distributary channel mouths. New land growth, in the form of emergent bars, can be mapped from a series of aerial-photo mosaics which span the 31-year period from 1954 to 1985. Sedimentation in these regions is governed by fluvial and marine processes operating within the seasonal cycles of winter freeze-up, spring break-up and summer open water. Each season is associated with characteristic thermal regimes, corresponding flow rates and independent sediment-transport processes.

During the winter season the Beaufort Sea and Mackenzie Delta are ice-covered and sediment/fluvial discharge through most delta channels is reduced by more than 80%. In deeper channels the ice cover confines the effluent into smaller sub-ice channels which scour beneath the bottomfast ice as conduits for winter discharge. Sedimentation in the Delta is negligible during this period.

Mackenzie River discharge and suspended-sediment concentrations increase rapidly during the spring break-up season in late-April. Fluvial discharge floods low-lying, protected islands at the delta front and bottomfast ice seaward of major distributary mouths, depositing fine sand. The largest percentage of the discharge however, is accommodated by existing sub-ice channels beneath the bottomfast ice zone. Because the sediment load is elevated during freshet, a large proportion of sediment by-passes the Delta and is transported offshore during break-up.

Deposition within the outer Delta is therefore largely restricted to the ice-free conditions of the summer open-water season. At this time of year water levels and suspended-sediment concentrations within outer delta channels are controlled by flood events originating in upstream tributaries and by storm surges generated offshore. Upstream storms introduce anomalously high concentrations of suspended sediment into the distributary channel network, independently of fluvial discharge. Northwesterly storms frequently elevate water levels by 75 cm or more resulting in extensive flooding of the outer Delta and a reversal in fluvial discharge which can be detected at least 12-km upstream. Deposition during such flood events leads to the gradual accretion of emergent bars and the infilling of smaller channels.

INTRODUCTION

The modern Mackenzie Delta is the largest arctic delta in North America. Situated along the northern edge of the Northwest Territories, the delta forms a 250-km long, 70-km wide complex of Holocene sediments deposited by the Mackenzie River. The coastal configuration of the Delta is characterized by drowned river mouths, breached thermokarst lakes and localized erosion rates which average 2 $m \cdot yr^{-1}$. Recent progradation of the delta appears to be relatively slow (Lewis and Forbes, 1975).

This paper focuses on sedimentary processes and the pattern of delta building at the mouth of Reindeer Channel, the third largest of four major distributaries of the Mackenzie Delta (Figure 1), to provide further insight into modern, river-dominated arctic delta development. The specific objectives of this paper are to summarize: (i) the annual cycle of sediment transport and deposition within the distributary mouth region, (ii) the resultant morphological evolution of the distributary mouth, and (iii) the effects of the fluvial system versus storms on sediment transport at the modern Mackenzie Delta-Beaufort Sea interface.

A more detailed discussion of these topics can be found in Jenner (1989).

SETTING

The study area is situated on the eastern margin of Shallow Bay at the mouth of Reindeer Channel and encompasses the Olivier Islands, an array of islands including Ellice, Pitt and "Stroud" Islands, and the primary network of "Ellice" and "Nonsuch" Channels which form a continuation of the parent Reindeer Channel (Figure 2). Like much of the outer Mackenzie Delta, the older Holocene islands (Ellice, "West" and Stroud) are characterized by low-lying tundra rarely exceeding 1 m in height, forming an abrupt wave-cut contact with the Beaufort Sea. Several younger islands consist of silt and very fine sand deposited via Ellice and Nonsuch

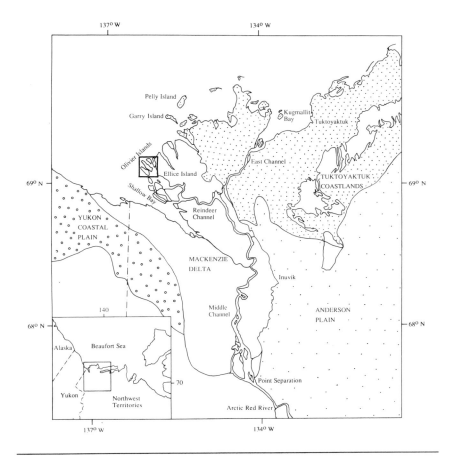

Figure 1. Location map showing the study area, the modern Mackenzie Delta, the four major distributaries of the Delta and the adjoining physiographic regions (after Rampton, 1988).

Channels in water depths less than 1.5 m. Seaward of the subaerial delta, a shallow platform less than 2-m deep extends more than 20-km offshore.

This shallow platform results from delta response to late Quaternary sea-level rise. The relative sea-level rise was caused by a combination of factors, the most significant being glacio-eustatic effects at the margin of the Wisconsin ice sheet (Forbes, 1980; Hill *et al.*, 1985).

Jenner and Hill

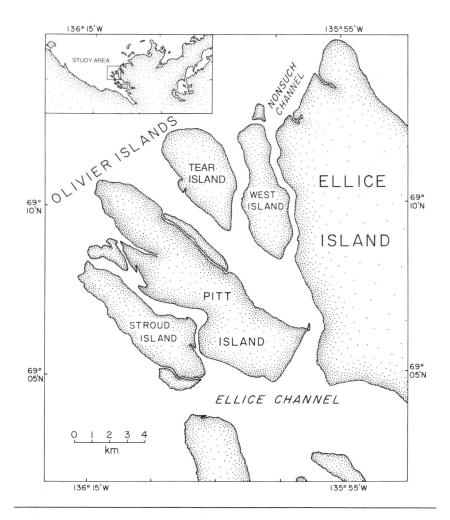

Figure 2. Detailed location map of the study area.

The very recent (late-Holocene) sea-level history can be inferred only from circumstantial evidence. The presence of barrier islands and spits along the Beaufort coast, the noticeable breaching of thermokarst lakes across the Tuktoyaktuk Peninsula, submerged peat beds within sectioned pingos (Mackay, 1963) and numerous drowned distributary channel mouths, appear to point to continuing submergence over the past 1,000 years.

METHODS

This paper summarizes the study of Jenner (1989) which was based on a six-week field program within the Olivier Islands from July 10 to August 20, 1987. Oceanographic work, which provides the basis for the paper, included the deployment of two Aanderaa current meters, Nisken water sampling, conductivity, temperature and depth (CTD) measurements, and bottom grab sampling. Details of the program can be found in Jenner (1989).

ARCTIC DELTA PROCESSES

Sedimentation within the Olivier Islands is governed by fluvial and marine processes operating within the seasonal cycles of winter freeze-up, spring break-up and summer open water. Each season is associated with characteristic thermal regimes, corresponding flow rates and independent sediment transport processes.

Winter Freeze-up

The freeze-up season begins in early October with the freeze-over of small lakes and the first signs of thin ice over larger lakes, channels and the nearshore coastal zone. By late-October to mid-November mean daily temperatures remain below 0°C and the delta plain and Beaufort Sea become completely ice-covered. For the next 7 months, sub-zero temperatures persist and Mackenzie River discharge is reduced by more than 80% of the average summer discharge (Figure 3).

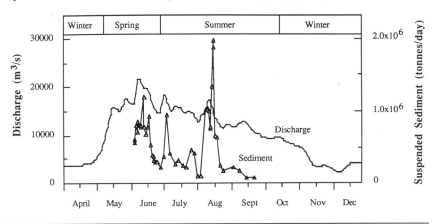

Figure 3. Mackenzie River discharge and suspended sediment concentrations measured at Arctic Red River from April to December, 1987. (Canada, Environment Canada, 1988a; 1988b)

Jenner and Hill

Spring Break-up

The break-up season within the Mackenzie Delta area lasts for 4 to 7 weeks, beginning in late-April or early-May and ending in mid- to late-June. During this period there is extensive flooding of low-lying areas at the delta coast immediately followed by the initial melting of winter ice.

The high spring river discharge and processes of ice break-up and coastal flooding make this the most hydrodynamically-active season of the high-latitude annual cycle. Two stages of ice break-up can be recognized (Figure 3). In early May there is a rapid increase in discharge and suspended-sediment concentrations (SSC), which accompany the initial period of flow and ice movement along shallow distributary channels. Delta front areas less than 1.0 m in height are flooded as large volumes of water become confined at the interface between river mouths and seaward bottomfast ice. The melting process continues until much of the ice has been cleared along major channel systems. Peak fluvial discharge associated with high concentrations of suspended sediment occurs in early-June and results from the annual melting of snow in the Mackenzie River drainage basin. The high volumes of fluvial discharge overflow bottomfast ice out to the 2-m isobath, accelerating the melting process. Delta-front flooding persists into late-June at which time the landfast ice is virtually melted and river discharge becomes moderated.

Summer Open Water

The open-water season begins in late-June, following the peak discharge period associated with freshet, and extends into late-October until the first signs of ice appear (Figure 3). During this portion of the annual cycle, the river regime, winds and waves dominate sediment transport and deposition and delta processes most closely approximate those of low-latitude delta systems.

Throughout the open-water season, Mackenzie River discharge into the Beaufort Sea is controlled by (i) hydrometeorological conditions originating in upstream tributaries (Lewis, 1988; Bigras, 1987) and (ii) storm-surge events at the distributary mouth. As shown in Figure 3 the Mackenzie River, at the Arctic Red River Water Survey of Canada station (Canada, Environment Canada, 1988a, 1988b), experiences a gradual decrease in flow and suspended-sediment concentrations (SSC) which are periodically interrupted by higher discharge fluctuations. The significant variation between flow and sediment discharge in mid-August is not unique to the summer of 1987 but is an annual, time variant characteristic of the Mackenzie River (Harper and Penland, 1982). Elevated SSC values recorded throughout the study area on August 17 are related to a heavy rainstorm event in the Liard River drainage basin which introduced anomalously high concentrations of suspended sediment into the Mackenzie River over a period of 3 to 4 days (K. Kranck and T. Milligan, pers. comm.). Such high suspended-sediment concentrations may additionally be enhanced by permafrost degradation during flooding, along channel banks.

At the coast, the warmer Mackenzie River discharge continues to melt back the polar ice pack offshore. Winds and waves then become the dominant mechanisms for sediment transport and deposition in the nearshore zone. The position of the ice edge, which ranges from 70-km seaward of the study area to 320 km (Fissel and Birch, 1984), governs the fetch available for wave generation. Under average conditions during the open-water season, wave heights range from 0.5 to 2 m. By August and September, when the polar ice pack is furthest seaward from the shoreline, long wind fetch creates wave heights in excess of 3 m during storm surges. These events increase water levels at the coast resulting in sediment erosion along exposed permafrost cliffs (Jenner, 1989; Forbes and Frobel, 1985; Rampton and Bouchard, 1975) and sediment resuspension and deposition along newly submerged sand bars (Jenner, 1989).

Throughout the open-water season there is an overall increase in the water level of Reindeer Channel, interrupted by abrupt, short-lived fluctuations of 50 to 60 cm. Examples of these storm-surge events can be seen in Figure 4b. By comparing these data

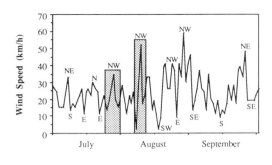

Figure 4a. Wind patterns measured from July to September, 1987 at Pelly Island, the closest weather monitoring station to the Olivier Islands (Canada, Environment Canada, 1987). Shaded areas represent the strong northwest wind events of July 28 and August 9.

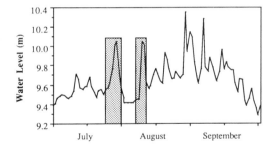

Figure 4b. Water levels recorded at Reindeer Channel from July to September, 1987 (Canada, Environment Canada, 1988b). Shaded areas represent water-level fluctuations of 50 cm on July 28 and August 9.

to the wind record in Figure 4a, a close correlation between wind direction and water level can be established. During extended periods of easterly and southerly winds, water levels within Reindeer Channel are lowered 10 to 20 cm below average

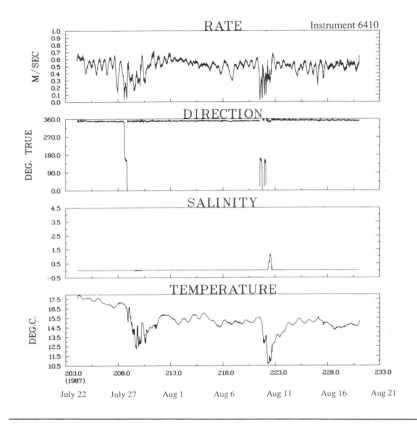

Figure 5. Flow rate, flow direction, salinity and temperature measurements recorded at the head of Nonsuch Channel from July 23 to August 20, 1987.

(e.g., August 3, Figure 4b). Alternately, north-westerly winds promote set-up along the coast resulting in rapid, positive water-level surges of up to 60 cm within the channel, as observed during July 28 and August 9, 1987 (Figure 4b).

This coastal set-up also influences the discharge characteristics of distributary channels. Under "fair" weather conditions the flow velocity of Nonsuch Channel fluctuates from 0.4 to 0.7 $m \cdot s^{-1}$ at the semidiurnal (M2) tidal frequency, with a mean flow rate of 0.6 $m \cdot s^{-1}$ (Figure 5). The effluent maintains an average temperature of 15.5°C and is completely fresh. Salinity measurements seaward from the mouth of Nonsuch Channel indicate that the channel effluent creates a coastal band of fresh water up to 20-km wide which prevents the influx of sea-water.

During summer storm events (e.g., July 28 and August 9, 1987) flow in the channel reverses and the gradual decrease in water temperatures within the channel, from 18 to 14.5°C, may be interrupted by large-scale temperature fluctuations of approximately 3°C (Figure 5). Corresponding salinity measurements reveal that a small, but nonetheless noticeable, saline intrusion was also detected at both instrument sites during the flow reversal of August 9.

MORPHOLOGICAL EVOLUTION OF THE OLIVIER ISLANDS

A 3-stage morphological evolution of the Olivier Islands is shown in the following series of vertical aerial photo mosaics spanning the period from 1954 to 1985. The formation of three sediment lobes confined by West and Stroud Islands was initiated sometime prior to the aerial photo coverage of 1954. By 1954 a pattern of subaerial land development was already established (Figure 6). Previously emergent sand bars had developed into vegetated subaerial islands. This growth phase was facilitated by small (less than 0.5-m deep) channels at the southwest ends of the islands which were responsible for sediment transport and deposition to the island interior during flood and storm surge periods. With the colonization of vege-

tation these new islands were able to withstand erosion and thus acted as a sediment trap for future deposition. Once stabilized, the sub-aerial islands began to increase in a lateral direction through deposition in quieter areas adjacent to the main channel flow during flow reversals.

By 1973 (Figure 7), new land growth had continued through the processes of lateral channel infilling and upstream island accretion. Previously emergent portions of the sediment lobes had developed into vegetated subaerial islands flanked by new emergent growth contiguous to

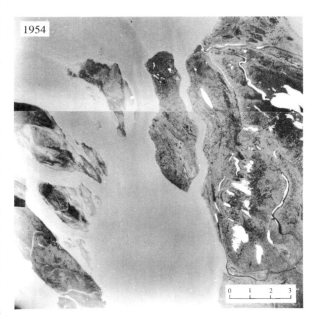

Figure 6. Vertical aerial photo mosaic of the study area taken during moderated water levels in July, 1954.

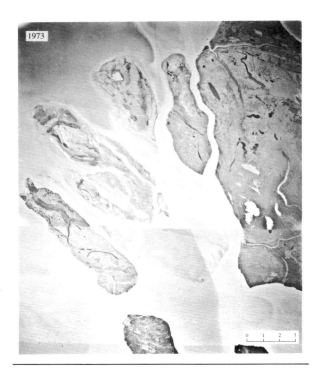

Figure 7. Vertical aerial photo mosaic of the study area taken during moderated water levels in August, 1973.

secondary channels. The secondary channel network had decreased in outlet width and the secondary channel once dividing Pitt Island had become sealed at its upstream end, providing a locus for further upstream sediment deposition. The upstream sealing of the secondary channel was probably facilitated by the 1970 storm surge.

Stage 3 (Figure 8) represents the maximum growth phase of the islands. Aerial photo mosaics confirm that prior to 1985 the landward growth of Pitt Island had reached the confines of Ellice and Nonsuch Channels and had become predominantly stabilized by vegetation. Subsequent to this growth stage, sand bars began to emerge at secondary channel mouths, further decreasing channel outlet widths within the remaining secondary channel network and restricting seaward sediment transport. By 1985, these processes appeared to have infilled the Olivier Islands region and a new phase of delta progradation commenced, as shown by the recent development of small emergent sand bars at the mouths of primary channels.

DISCUSSION

Sediment transport and deposition within the Olivier Islands are predominantly confined to the break-up and summer open-water seasons. Heavy rainfall caused by storms in upstream distributaries, and coastal storm surges form the primary controls on water levels, discharge, sediment discharge, sediment reworking and river-mouth processes. The response of each of these processes during storm surges modifies normal sediment-distribution patterns within the distributary mouth and appears to be responsible for the characteristic upstream growth-style of the islands.

Sediment discharge to the distributary mouth is primarily controlled by flooding associated with storms in upstream distributaries. The Liard River event emphasizes the independent relationship which exists between SSC and fluvial discharge and shows that anomalously high concentrations of suspended sediment can be transported during moderated water levels. This process therefore, may result in enhanced sediment deposition along shallow submerged banks in quieter areas adjacent to the main flow. If these high SSC events coincide with coastal storm surges significantly high rates of upstream sedimentation are likely to occur.

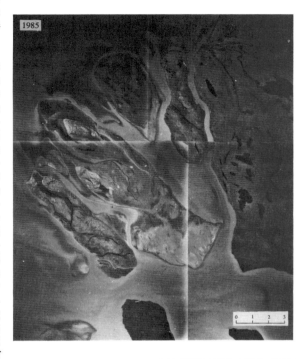

Figure 8. Vertical aerial photo mosaic of the study area taken in August, 1985 during moderate to low water levels.

The direct effects of coastal storm surges are most pronounced in the subaerial environment. Water level surges of 60 to 70 cm completely submerge low-lying, partially-vegetated islands. Waves generated by the storms average 0.5 to 1.0 m high over the submergent features, resulting in bottom sediment resuspension and local coastal erosion of up to 1.0 m along contiguous, exposed islands. Eroded material from these areas is transported several kilometres upstream by flow reversals detected as far as 12 km from the channel mouth. Much of the coastally-derived sediment is redeposited at upstream locations perhaps during semidiurnal flood tides which reduce the flow rate to $0.1 \ \text{m} \cdot \text{s}^{-1}$.

The secondary effect of coastal storm surges is the introduction of saline water into the distributary mouth. The low salinities observed during storm surges probably have little effect on river-mouth processes because bottom frictional

Jenner and Hill

processes would still be dominant in the shallow water depths seaward of the channel mouth. However, the introduction of brackish water from a distance of 20-km offshore, emphasizes the intensity of flow reversals created by water-level rises of less than 75 cm and highlights the potential for onshore sediment transport into the shallow distributary mouth environment during larger surges.

While the normal processes of sediment transport and deposition are frequently interrupted by summer storms, the system recovers subsequent to the passage of a storm, resulting in gradual lateral and upstream morphological modification of the islands as observed by a comparison of the aerial photo mosaics representing stage 2 (1954) and stage 3 (1973) of the Olivier Islands evolution. Storms with much greater return periods, such as the 1970 storm however, cause rapid catastrophic change in the shallow distributary mouth environment, which in the case of the sealing of the secondary channel within Pitt Island, prevents recovery of the system by disrupting the sediment balance.

CONCLUSIONS

1. The Olivier Islands represent a localized phase of sedimentation within the overall transgressive framework of the Mackenzie Delta.

2. Sediment transport and deposition are predominantly confined to a four-month, ice-free, summer open-water season. Water levels, discharge, sediment discharge and river-mouth processes during this season are controlled by heavy rainfall in upstream distributaries and coastal storm surges. Upstream flooding introduces anomalously high concentrations of suspended sediment to the distributary mouth during moderated water levels. Coastal storms elevate water levels resulting in bottom sediment resuspension, local coastal erosion, the introduction of offshore brackish water into the distributary channel, and upstream sediment transport during flow reversals.

3. The unique upstream style of sedimentation characteristic of the Olivier Islands reflects storm-related deposition during the latter part of the summer open water season when storm duration and intensity are highest.

REFERENCES

BIGRAS, S.C., 1987. Lake regimes, Mackenzie Delta, N.W.T., 1984. NHRI Contribution No.87005, Surface Water Division, National Hydrology Research Institute, Environment Canada, Saskatoon, Saskatchewan, April, 52 pp.

CANADA, ENVIRONMENT CANADA, 1987. Unpublished wind directions and wind speeds from Pelly Island, Northwest Territories, for July, August and September, 1987. Atmospheric Environment Service, Edmonton, Alberta

CANADA, ENVIRONMENT CANADA, 1988a. Sediment data: Yukon and Northwest Territories, 1987. Water Survey of Canada, Water Resources Branch, Inland Waters Directorate, Environment Canada, Ottawa, Ontario, 18 pp.

CANADA, ENVIRONMENT CANADA, 1988b. Surface water data - Yukon and Northwest Territories, 1987. Water Survey of Canada, Water Resources Branch, Inland Waters Directorate, Environment Canada, Ottawa, Ontario, 110 pp.

FISSEL, D.B. and J.R. BIRCH, 1984. Sediment transport in the Canadian Beaufort Sea. Unpublished report, Arctic Sciences Limited, Sidney, B.C. to the Geological Survey of Canada, Dartmouth, Nova Scotia, Open File No.35-060-F, 165 pp.

FORBES, D.L., 1980. Late Quaternary sea levels in the southern Beaufort Sea. In - Current Research, Part B, GSC Paper No.80-1B, Geological Survey of Canada, Ottawa, Ontario, 75-87

FORBES, D.L. and D. FROBEL, 1985. Coastal erosion and sedimentation in the Canadian Beaufort Sea. In - Current Research, GSC Paper No.85-1B, Geological Survey of Canada, Ottawa, Ontario, 69-80

HARPER, J.R. and S. PENLAND, 1982. Beaufort Sea sediment dynamics. Unpublished report, Woodward-Clyde Consultants, Victoria, B.C., to the Geological Survey of Canada, Dartmouth, Nova Scotia, 125 pp.

HILL, P.R., P.J. MUDIE, K. MORAN and S.M. BLASCO, 1985. A sea-level curve for the Canadian Beaufort Shelf. Canadian Journal of Earth Sciences, 22(10), 1383-1393

JENNER, K.A., 1989. Modern deltaic sedimentation in an arctic setting: Olivier Islands, Mackenzie Delta, Northwest Territories. M.Sc. thesis, Department of Geology, Dalhousie University, Halifax, Nova Scotia, 119 pp.

LEWIS, C.P., 1988. Mackenzie Delta sedimentary environments and processes. Draft Contract Report to Sediment Survey Section, Water Resources Branch, Inland Waters Directorate, Environment Canada, Ottawa, Ontario, January 26, 395 pp.

LEWIS, C.P. and D.L. FORBES, 1975. Coastal sedimentary processes and sediments, southern Canadian Beaufort Sea. Beaufort Sea Technical Report No.24, Beaufort Sea Project, Department of the Environment, Victoria, B.C., 68 pp.

MACKAY, J.R., 1963. The Mackenzie Delta area, N.W.T. Geographical Branch Memoir No.8, Department of Mines and Technical Surveys, Ottawa, Ontario, 202 pp.

RAMPTON, V.N., 1988. Quaternary geology of the Tuktoyaktuk Coastlands, Northwest Territories. GSC Memoir No.423, Geological Survey of Canada, Ottawa, Ontario, 98 pp.

RAMPTON, V.N. and M. BOUCHARD, 1975. Surficial geology of Tuktoyaktuk, District of Mackenzie. GSC Paper No.74-53, Geological Survey of Canada, Ottawa, Ontario, 17 pp.

DISCHARGE AND SEDIMENT REGIMES OF LAKE CHANNEL SYSTEMS IN THE MACKENZIE DELTA, N.W.T.*

M. Ferguson and P. Marsh

National Hydrology Research Institute
11 Innovation Boulevard
Saskatoon, Saskatchewan
S7N 3H5   CANADA

ABSTRACT

The input of water and sediment into lakes in the Mackenzie Delta is controlled primarily by the lake sill elevation and the distance of the lake from the main channels. However, there are important processes which complicate this apparently simple system. For example, while the frequency and duration of flooding of all lakes is controlled primarily by sill elevation, there are variations in lake regime between lakes with similar sill elevations. This variation is due to differences between single lakes which are connected directly to the main channels, and lakes which are part of large, connected lake systems. A further complication, is that the definition of distance between the lake and main channel is related to channel distance, not to physical distance. Since the flow directions in large lake systems varies during the summer period, lakes may be "close" to the main channel for part of the summer and "far" away for the remainder of the summer. As a result, it is often impossible to classify lakes from air photos or even from limited field data.

Since spring break-up results in the highest water levels of the year, it is often assumed that the suspended-sediment concentrations are also the highest of the year. As data for 1987 clearly shows, this is not always the case. In fact, summer rainstorm events may result in significantly higher concentrations than those occurring during the spring melt period.

INTRODUCTION

The Mackenzie Delta is a complex array of lakes, channels, flood plains and levees, each of which is associated with a particular assemblage of vegetation. Despite its northern latitude, this ecosystem is very productive and supports large populations of birds, fish and mammals. As a result, the delta is important to the people of the area for both fishing and trapping, and as a source of freshwater.

---

*National Hydrology Research Institute Contribution Series Number CS-89056.

Lakes play an extremely important role in the Mackenzie Delta ecosystem. They cover approximately 25% of the delta area and provide significant habitat for fish, birds, and mammals. They also act as sinks for sediment entering the Delta and therefore play an important role in its evolution. The relatively high biological productivity of these lakes is due primarily to the dynamic variations in water level, and the large fluxes of sediment and nutrients into the lakes. Despite the importance of sediments to the delta system, few studies have attempted to measure lake sedimentation rates or to measure the flux of sediment through lake channels. For example, Mackay (1963) and Gill (1971) have used sedimentation plates, while Cordes and McLennan (1984) utilized ^{137}Cs dating to determine sedimentation rates. These data have shown variable sedimentation rates, but their usefulness has been limited by temporal and spatial constraints.

It is often postulated that lakes in the Mackenzie Delta are sensitive to environmental changes. Changes in the hydrological regime due to flow regulation, diversion, or climate change could impact the hydrological and sedimentation regimes of delta lakes, and consequently their biological productivity. In addition, continuing oil and gas production and exploration will result in increased hydrocarbon contamination of the Mackenzie River. Since hydrocarbons attach themselves preferentially to fine-grained sediments, these pollutants will find their way into delta lakes creating unknown environmental problems.

Despite the importance of lakes to the delta ecosystem and their potential sensitivity to environmental degradation, complicated interrelationships between the hydrological, geomorphological, and biological components are not well understood. The goal of this paper, therefore, is to improve our understanding of one aspect of these interrelationships, the hydrological and sediment regime of delta lakes. In particular, this study will look at temporal and spatial variations in water and sediment fluxes through the channel systems of three delta lakes near Inuvik.

MACKENZIE DELTA EVOLUTION

The evolution of the Mackenzie Delta is controlled by a delicate balance between sediment input, the direction and rates of sea-level change, the pattern of coastal erosion and the rates of permafrost aggradation or degradation (Carson, 1988). Only a few studies have attempted to consolidate the available information in order to develop a scenario of delta evolution. Mackay (1963), and Johnston and Brown (1965) were among the first to attempt this. They utilized observations from a cut bank along East Channel, from drill-hole stratigraphy near Inuvik, and from sediment cores from "NRC" lake, to suggest that the delta has prograded and aggraded relatively quickly in an environment characterized by constant sea levels over the last 7,000 to 8,000 years. More recent work has shown that sea levels have not been constant, but in fact have been rising at a rate of 0.38 to 0.71 m/century (Carson, 1988). Lewis (1988) uses this recent evidence in addition to the work of Mackay (1963) and Johnston and Brown (1965) to develop a different scenario. He hypothesizes that the Delta has undergone both transgressional and aggradational evolution. However, he states that due to the lack of data from sites within the Delta, the matter is still not settled.

STUDY SITES AND HYDROLOGICAL REGIME

The study area, located in the upper Mackenzie Delta, is approximately 5 km southwest of Inuvik (Figure 1) at 68°19'N and 133°50'W. It is an area of poorly-developed levees with floodplains which are older and higher than those in more northerly portions of the delta. This area is in the zone of continuous permafrost, but the ground beneath the lakes is completely unfrozen (Johnston and Brown, 1964). The vegetation surrounding the lakes is a mature spruce forest progressing to alder and willow stands closer to the water level and equisetum stands at and below water level.

The hydrological regime of delta lakes in this area is dominated by flooding by the Mackenzie River with the frequency and duration of lake flooding controlled by the water level of the Delta main channels and by the lake sill elevation, where lake sill elevation is defined as the highest elevation along the channel thalweg connecting the lake and main channel. For all lakes, water enters from the Mackenzie River only when main channel levels are above the lake sills. During this period, water flow into or out of the lakes is controlled by water-level differences between the distributary and the lake, with water moving into the lake during periods of rising main channel stage and flow out of the lake during falling stage. Since lake sills vary over a range of approximately 5 m, the frequency and duration of lake flooding vary greatly (Marsh and Hey, 1989).

The three lakes with unofficial names of "Skidoo", "South" and "NRC" and their four channels; South Lake Channel, Skidoo Channel East, Skidoo Channel West, and NRC Channel were studied (Figure 1). These lake/channel systems are representative of the range of lake types in this portion of the Mackenzie Delta.

NRC Lake is approximately 0.069 km^2 in area, with a mean depth of 0.88 m and a maximum depth of 1.6 m in mid-summer. Due to the existence of permafrost, which extends down to bedrock around the perimeter of the lake, NRC Lake is perched above the surrounding lakes and channels with a sill elevation of approximately 3.8 m a.s.l. (Marsh, 1986). As a result, water and sediment flux into and out of the lake is limited to the spring-flood and flood-recession times. Since the sill is located between North Lake and NRC Lake (Figure 1), NRC Lake does not receive water directly from a main channel. Instead, water passes through the series of lakes immediately north of NRC Lake. It would be expected that this would result in lower sediment inputs to NRC Lake.

South Lake is approximately 0.38 km^2 in area, with a maximum depth of 4 m in mid-summer and a sill elevation of only 1.3 m a.s.l. (Marsh, 1986). Unlike NRC Lake, South Lake is connected to the main channel system by a single channel which

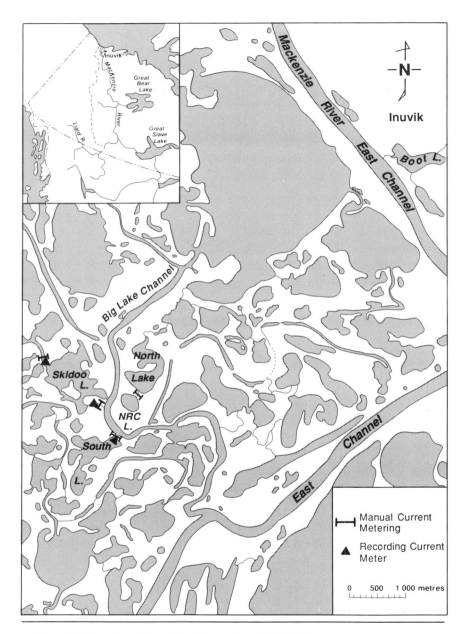

Figure 1. Location of the study site near Inuvik, N.W.T.

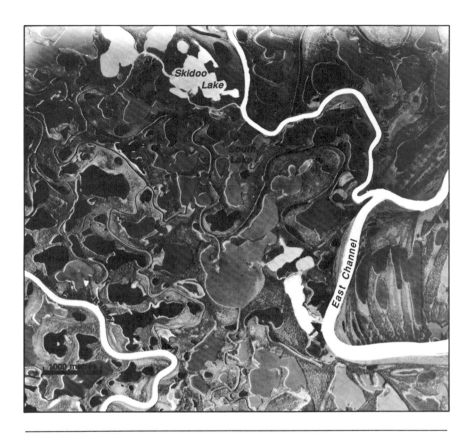

Figure 2. Aerial photograph showing Skidoo Lake connections (▸) to Big Lake Channel, East Channel and Rabbit Ears Channel.

is connected directly to Big Lake Channel (Figure 1). It would be expected therefore that the sediment input would be considerably higher than for NRC Lake.

Skidoo Lake, approximately 0.62 km^2 in area with a maximum mid-summer depth of 4 m, is the first in a series of lakes which are connected to Big Lake Channel by Skidoo Channel East and to East Channel and Rabbit Ears Channel by Skidoo Channel West (Figure 2). The flooding regime of Skidoo Lake is similar to South Lake, but is further complicated since it is part of a large multi-channel/lake system. During the summer months, flow reversals are influenced not only by Big Lake Channel water levels, but also by water levels in both East and Rabbit Ears

Ferguson and Marsh

channels. The sediment regime of Skidoo Lake is also affected by this multi-channel/lake system.

An important feature in Skidoo and South Lakes are the lake deltas located where the channels enter into the lakes. NRC does not have a lake delta.

METHODOLOGY

The measurement of discharge in each of the study channels is complicated by the fact that flow direction changes frequently during the summer. Since these flow reversals may occur at any water elevation or stage, a standard stage-discharge rating curve cannot be used. This problem was overcome in the following ways. First, channel discharge was measured four times per week using a standard Price-type current meter at regular intervals across each of the four study channels (Figure 1) with discharge into the lake being recorded as positive and out of the lake as negative flow. Although this sampling interval was not sufficiently frequent to document all flow reversals, it was felt that because reversals are driven by slow changes in the Mackenzie River stage it was sufficient to document the majority of flow reversals. In order to enhance the manual measurements, submersible recording current meters were installed at Skidoo channels East and West, and South Lake Channel. These instruments recorded mean hourly values of point velocity and water depth, and hourly values of instantaneous flow direction. Mean channel velocity for the entire cross section was then obtained by regressing point velocity from the recording current meter versus mean cross sectional velocity as measured from the manual current meter. Channel cross-sectional area was calculated by regressing point water depth versus the cross-sectional areas measured at the times of the manual current-meter measurements. Daily discharge was then calculated by summing the product of the hourly mean cross-sectional velocity, flow direction and cross-sectional area.

Unfortunately, the recording current meter for South Lake Channel experienced a data-logger failure and the velocity cups on the meter in Skidoo Channel West were slowed by sediment accumulation. As a result, only the discharge for Skidoo Channel East was calculated from the recording current-meter data, while the daily discharge for Skidoo Channel West and South Lake Channel were calculated from the manual discharge measurements. These instantaneous values were assumed to be representative of average daily values.

Suspended-sediment samples were obtained at each site during the spring break-up, when the channels were partially ice-covered, using grab samples taken from a helicopter. Once boat travel was possible, manual suspended-sediment sampling was conducted using the US-DH 48 depth-integrating, hand-operated wading sampler coincident to discharge measurements at Skidoo channels East and West, South Lake Channel, and NRC Channel. The representativeness of these samples was checked by carrying out detailed measurements of vertical, cross-channel and hourly variations in suspended-sediment concentration. This detailed sampling showed little variation in concentration between the bottom and the top of the profile, which is typical of wash-load movement (Richards, 1982). This wash-load characteristic and the absence of diurnal fluctuations eliminated the need for more frequent or more detailed suspended-sediment sampling.

Suspended-sediment samples were analyzed following the procedure outlined by Stainton *et al.* (1977). A known volume of sample (250 mL was used except in the case of very high or low concentrations when volumes were adjusted to optimize filtering speed and sediment weight captured) was filtered through pre-dried and weighed Whatman GF/C 42.5-mm diameter glass microfiber filter papers with an effective retention of 1.2 μm (Fisher Scientific, 1987). The sediment concentration was then determined from the dry solid weight divided by the sample volume.

Bed-material movement was measured using a Bogardi Sampler, which is a pressure-difference type of sampler suitable for use with fine materials. Measurements were obtained during a summer peak event in August. The sampler was placed on the bed of Skidoo Channel East during a period when flow was positive. During a 1-hour time interval, 2 g of material moved as bed load over the channel compared to a suspended sediment load of approximately 3,000 kg·hr^{-1}. This indicated that bed-material movement represents a small portion of the total sediment movement along channels, and therefore could be ignored for the remainder of the study.

ANALYSIS AND DISCUSSION

The seasonal variations in discharge, suspended sediment and water level for each of the study channels are shown in Figures 3 to 6. All four channels show a peak in suspended-sediment concentration and water level during the spring break-up period, May 30 to June 14 (Day 150 to 165). Not shown on the graphs are the peaks in channel discharge into the lakes which would be coincident with the rapid rise in lake levels during this period. The peak water level at Inuvik was 5.570 m a.s.l. on June 4 (Day 155). This water level, with a return period of 2.2 years, is close to the mean of 5.636 m a.s.l. (Marsh and Hey, 1989) suggesting that sediment movement, since it is closely related to water level and velocity, should be typical as well (Richards, 1982).

During the spring break-up period, the water level and sediment regimes of South Channel and Skidoo Channel East are similar. At both sites, the water overtops the low sills in mid-May and flows from Big Lake Channel over the ice blocking the channels and into the lake. During this period the discharge into each lake is low, but it rapidly increases with rising stage in Big Lake Channel. Initially the suspended-sediment concentrations of the water flowing in South and Skidoo East channels are also low (Figures 4a, 5a), due to the low sediment concentrations in the main channels. However, the sediment input to the lakes soon begins to increase rapidly as suspended sediment in the main channels rises in response to the rapidly-increasing input from the southern portions of the Mackenzie basin. The peak

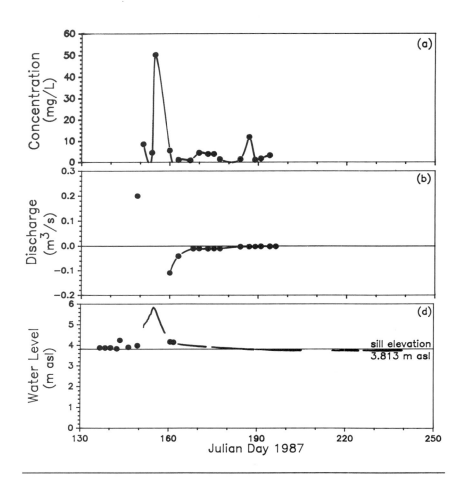

Figure 3. Suspended-sediment concentration, discharge and water level for NRC Lake Channel. Note that positive values are for flow into the lake and negative out of the lake.

suspended-sediment concentrations during the spring break-up are near the highest of the year, with values of near 550 mg·L^{-1} in South Lake Channel, and 375 mg·L^{-1} in Skidoo Channel East. Concentrations are generally lower in Skidoo Channel East than in South Lake Channel because the channel is longer, allowing sedimentation to occur along the channel prior to the water entering Skidoo Lake.

At both Skidoo East and South Lake channels, the suspended-sediment concentration peaked on May 29, prior to the maximum water level on June 3. A

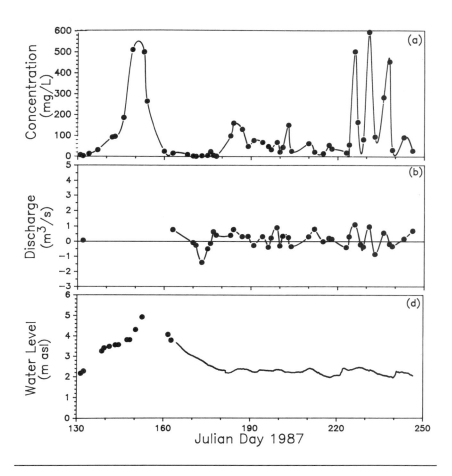

Figure 4. Suspended-sediment concentration, discharge and water level for South Lake Channel. Note that positive values are for flow into the lake and negative out of the lake.

similar phenomenon was observed in the Colville River Delta in Alaska by Arnborg *et al.* (1967) and explained as follows. The lag between peak sediment and water level was due primarily to changes in the sediment supply during the period of rapidly rising water levels. During the initial rise in water levels, sediments were flushed out of mudbars and gullies. As this initial source was depleted, river-bank erosion became significant, but it was not as great as that initially removed from the mudbars and gullies.

Ferguson and Marsh

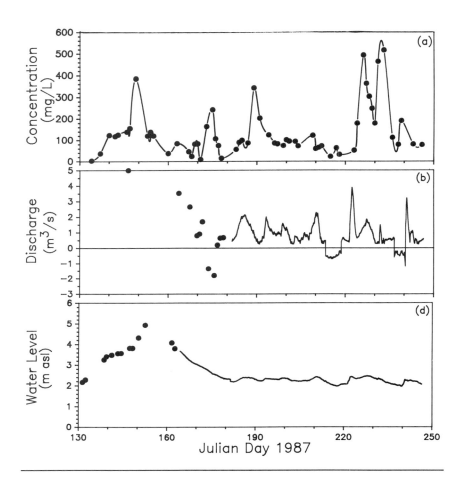

Figure 5. Suspended-sediment concentration, discharge and water level for Skidoo Channel East. Note that positive values are for flow into the lake and negative out of the lake.

During the period of rising stage in the spring, water flows out of Skidoo Lake and through Skidoo Channel West into the other lakes in the Skidoo system. Due to its distance from a main channel and settling of sediment in Skidoo Lake, Skidoo Channel West has a lower suspended-sediment concentration than Skidoo Channel East (Figures 5a, 6a).

After the peak water level is reached, main channel water levels drop rapidly (Figure 4c), with resulting discharge out of the lakes. For South Lake, water is

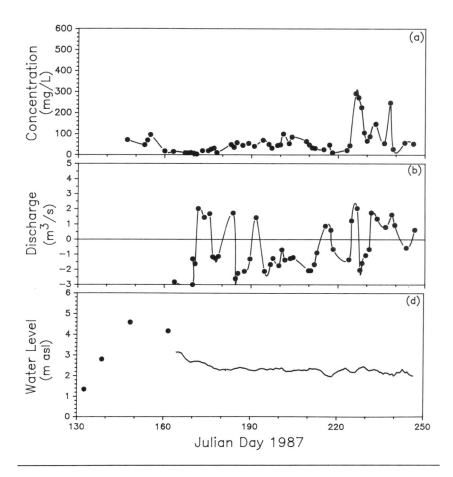

Figure 6. Suspended-sediment concentration, discharge and water level for Skidoo Channel West. Note that positive values are for flow into the lake and negative out of the lake.

simply discharged out of South Lake Channel. For Skidoo Lake, water generally continues to flow into the lake through Skidoo East, with larger discharge out of Skidoo West. During this period of falling water levels, the suspended-sediment concentrations also decline rapidly (Figures 3a, 4a, 5a, 6a).

During the remainder of the summer, the discharge regime of South and Skidoo Lake channels is dominated by small fluctuations in the water level of Big Lake Channel. However, the two lakes respond very differently. Since South Lake is

Ferguson and Marsh

connected to Big Lake Channel by a single channel, it responds quickly to changes in main distributary level, with rapid changes between positive and negative discharge (Figure 4b). During the 1987 season there were 10 inflow events to South Lake. This is approximately normal for lakes with the sill elevation of South Lake (Marsh and Hey, 1989). Skidoo Lake also responds to changes in Big Lake Channel levels, with rapid changes in discharge (Figure 5b). However, the flow is generally into the lake through Skidoo East, and with discharge in Skidoo West fluctuating between into and out of the lake (Figure 6b). In Skidoo Channel East there were only a few negative discharges during periods of low water level. A total of only four inflows through Skidoo Channel East is considerably different from that occurring in South Lake, even though Skidoo Lake has a sill elevation similar to South Lake.

The complexities of the discharge regime of the Skidoo Lake system are illustrated in Figure 7. On June 18, the flow was from Big Lake Channel into Skidoo Lake and then out through Far Lake. Discharge was also out of the lake system to the south. On August 11 flow was in the same direction through Skidoo Lake, but note that flow directions had reversed at the other two channel sites. Later in the summer (September 3) flow reversed in Skidoo Channel East and West, but the other two sites remained as they were on June 18. These data illustrate the complexity of the Skidoo Lake system, with flow directions in Skidoo East and West controlled not only by Big Lake Channel water levels, but also by levels in the lakes within the system, and by East Channel and Rabbit Ears Channel. Since these channels have very low slopes, it is difficult to measure the changes in levels responsible for these fluctuations in discharge. As a result, flow directions are difficult to predict.

In conjunction with these variations in discharge during the summer period, there were also large fluctuations in suspended-sediment concentrations in South and Skidoo Lake Channels (Figures 4, 5, 6). Flow into the lakes generally had higher suspended-sediment concentrations due to the effect of the main channels, while the outflow had lower values due to settling of sediment in the lake basins. The general pattern is the same for South Lake and Skidoo East and West, with values fluctuating between 2 and 300 $mg \cdot L^{-1}$ during much of the summer. This pattern is also illustrated in Figure 7, where the suspended-sediment concentration decreases with increasing distance along the Skidoo Lake system. Figures 4-6 also show that suspended sediment increased dramatically during August (days 226 to 232, August 14 to August 20) with peak suspended-sediment values of 567 $mg \cdot L^{-1}$ in Skidoo Channel East (Figure 5a). This event was caused by a storm in the upper Liard basin. Precipitation during July in the upper Liard was above average and, with the precipitation from this August event (Canada, Environment Canada, 1988a), higher discharges (Canada, Environment Canada, 1988b) and suspended-sediment concentration were recorded along the Liard and Mackenzie Rivers. Although this event resulted in dramatic increases in suspended-sediment concentrations, it resulted in only small increases in water levels in the Delta (Figures 4c, 5c, 6c).

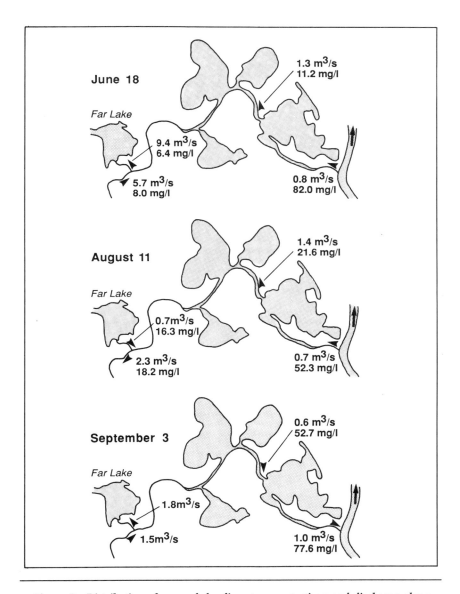

Figure 7. Distribution of suspended-sediment concentrations and discharge along Skidoo Channel system during three periods in 1987.

Ferguson and Marsh

The discharge and sediment regime of NRC Lake is different from both Skidoo and South lakes in two respects. First, the high sill of NRC Lake limits the flooding of the lake to maximum flood stage only (Figure 3). Discharge is into the lake during the rapid rise in levels in the spring and then out of the lake during the remainder of the summer, with discharge ceasing in mid-summer (Figure 3b). Thus sediment is transported into the lake only during the brief period of rising stage in the spring. Second, NRC Lake is the last lake in a series of lakes, and therefore does not receive flood water directly from a main distributary. As a result, the suspended-sediment concentration of the water entering NRC Lake is considerably lower, with peak concentrations of only 50 mg·L^{-1} (Figure 3a) compared to over 500 mg·L^{-1} at South Lake.

These complexities in discharge and suspended-sediment concentrations have implications to the feasibility of using the Cordes and McLennan (1984) lake-classification system, where lakes are classified by their flooding regime and sedimentation rate, with the sedimentation rate approximated by the "closeness" of a lake to a main channel. It is assumed that lakes "close" to a main channel have higher sedimentation rates than lakes which are "far" away from a main channel. In a general sense this is true, but the difficulty in applying this system is clearly demonstrated by the Skidoo Lake and NRC Lake examples. At certain times of the year Skidoo Lake is "close" to the main distributary (the flow is from Big Lake Channel along Skidoo Channel East and into Skidoo Lake), while at other times of the year Skidoo Lake is "distant" from the main sediment source (flow is from other parts of the system through Skidoo Channel West and into the lake). Without detailed field measurements, it would be very difficult to determine if a lake like Skidoo Lake was in fact "close to" or "far away" from a main channel. In addition, NRC Lake would also be difficult to fit into the Cordes and McLennan (1984) classification system. NRC's physical location is very close to Big Lake Channel but the "hydrological" distance is much longer as flood water must flow through Big Lake, North Lake and then into NRC Lake (Figure 1). These examples clearly illustrate that ground surveys are required to determine the "hydrological" distance from a main distributary. Otherwise, the "close" and "far" classification system would be difficult to apply to certain lakes.

CONCLUSION

The data presented here illustrate the following important aspects of the temporal variation of sediment and water movement into and out of typical lakes in the central portion of the Mackenzie Delta:

(1)   The duration and frequency of lake flooding by the Mackenzie River is dependent on lake sill elevation, but the specific characteristics of flooding for lakes with the same sill elevation can vary greatly depending on whether the lake is connected directly to a main channel, or is part of a series of lakes. For example, South Lake and Skidoo Lake have similar sill elevations, but their hydrographs are very different, with South Lake

experiencing a number of inflow/outflow events, while Skidoo Lake experienced far fewer events. This has important implications to the lake sediment balance and the input of pollutants to the lake.

(2) The suspended-sediment concentration of water entering into lakes is highly variable. Lakes which are "close" to a main channel have much larger sediment concentrations. However, the term "close" refers to flow distance, not straight-line distance. In fact, a lake may be "physically" close to a main channel, but far away from the main channel in terms of channel flow distance. In addition, because of changes in flow direction in large lake systems, lakes may be "close" to a main channel for part of the year, and "far" away during the remainder of the year. Due to these complexities, it is very difficult to classify the sediment regime of lakes from air photos alone.

(3) Although the spring break-up event always has the highest water levels of the year, the suspended-sediment concentrations may be larger during summer rainfall events than during the spring break-up period.

REFERENCES

ARNBORG, L., H.J. WALKER and J. PEIPPO, 1967. Suspended load in the Colville River, Alaska, 1962. Geografiska Annaler, 49A(2-4), 131-144

CANADA, ENVIRONMENT CANADA, 1988a. Monthly record - Meteorological observations in Canada. Atmospheric Environment Service, Environment Canada, Downsview, Ontario, microfiches

CANADA, ENVIRONMENT CANADA, 1988b. Surface water data - Yukon and Northwest Territories, 1987. Water Survey of Canada, Water Resources Branch, Inland Waters Directorate, Environment Canada, Ottawa, Ontario, 110 pp.

CARSON, M.A., 1988. An assessment of problems relating to the source, transfer and fate of sediment along the Mackenzie River, N.W.T. Contract Report No.WPM-88-006 to Sediment Survey Section, Water Resources Branch, and Western and Northern Region, Water Planning and Management Branch, Inland Waters Directorate, Environment Canada, 115 pp.

CORDES, L.D. and D.S. McLENNAN, 1984. The estimation of sedimentation rates using ^{137}Cs in lakes of the Mackenzie Delta. Unpublished report, L. Cordes and Associates, Calgary, Alberta for British Columbia Power and Hydro Authority, Vancouver, British Columbia, August 27, 68 pp.

FISHER SCIENTIFIC, 1987. Fisher 87/RS. Fisher Scientific, Ottawa, Ontario, 1384 pp.

GILL, D., 1971. Vegetation and environment in the Mackenzie River Delta, N.W.T.: a study in subarctic ecology. Ph.D. thesis, Department of Geography, University of British Columbia, Vancouver, B.C., 694 pp.

JOHNSTON, G.H. and R.J.E. BROWN, 1964. Some observations on permafrost distribution at a lake in the Mackenzie Delta, N.W.T., Canada. Arctic, 17(3), 163-175

JOHNSTON, G.H. and R.J.E. BROWN, 1965. Stratigraphy of the Mackenzie River delta, Northwest Territories, Canada. Geological Society of America Bulletin, 76(1), 103-112

LEWIS, C.P., 1988. Mackenzie Delta sedimentary environments and processes. Draft Contract Report to Sediment Survey Section, Water Resources Branch, Inland Waters Directorate, Environment Canada, Ottawa, Ontario, January 26, 395 pp.

MACKAY, J.R., 1963. The Mackenzie Delta area, N.W.T. Geographical Branch Memoir No.8, Department of Mines and Technical Surveys, Ottawa, Ontario, 202 pp.

MARSH, P., 1986. Modelling water levels for a lake in the Mackenzie Delta. Proceedings of the Symposium: Cold Regions Hydrology, D.L. Kane (Editor), 22-25 July 1986, Fairbanks, Alaska, American Water Resources Association Technical Publication Series No.TPS-86-1, Bethesda, Maryland, 23-29

MARSH, P. and M. HEY, 1989. The flooding hydrology of Mackenzie Delta lakes near Inuvik, N.W.T., Canada. Arctic, 42(1), 41-49

RICHARDS, K., 1982. Rivers: form and process in alluvial channels. Methuen & Co., New York, N.Y., 358 pp.

STAINTON, M.P., M.J. CAPEL and F.A.J. ARMSTRONG, 1977. The chemical analysis of freshwater. Miscellaneous Special Publication No.25, Fisheries and Marine Service, Fisheries and Environment Canada, 2nd edition, Freshwater Institute, Winnipeg, Manitoba, 180 pp.

BIOLOGICAL PROCESSES

NET COMMUNITY PHOTOSYNTHESIS IN MACKENZIE DELTA LAKES NEAR INUVIK, N.W.T.

R.E. Hecky, R.H. Hesslein and P.S. Ramlal

Department of Fisheries and Oceans
Freshwater Institute
501 University Crescent
Winnipeg, Manitoba
R3T 2N6   CANADA

ABSTRACT

Photosynthesis of the different plant communities of four delta lakes with varying degrees of closure was measured in 1986. Radiocarbon techniques were applied to algal communities while macrophyte communities were estimated with harvest techniques. In 1987 CO_2 fluxes between air and water, and sediments and water, were used to estimate whole-lake net photosynthesis in the same lakes during the growing season of June through August. Less than a two-fold range in phytoplankton areal photosynthetic rates was observed between turbid, channel-connected "Skidoo Lake" and the clearest lakes. However areal-macrophyte net photosynthesis varied by over a factor of 20 in these same lakes. Total net photosynthesis ranged form 2 to 3 mmoles $C·m^{-2}·d^{-1}$ in the most turbid lake to >60 mmoles $C·m^{-2}·d^{-1}$ in high-closure, clear "NRC Lake". In the turbid lake, algae account for most of the photosynthesis while in clear lakes they account for less than 5% of community photosynthesis. The availability of light strongly controls algal and submerged-macrophyte photosynthesis. These independent methods concur quantitatively on rates of community photosynthesis in delta lakes. Despite the dominance of community photosynthesis by macrophytes, stable-isotope analysis of the aquatic food chain indicates that these higher plants are not the most important source of energy-sustaining fish production.

PHYTOPLANKTON COMPOSITION, PHOTOSYNTHESIS, AND NUTRIENT STATUS IN LAKES AND CHANNELS IN THE MACKENZIE DELTA, N.W.T.

S.J. Guildford, E.J. Fee and H.J. Kling

Department of Fisheries and Oceans
Freshwater Institute
501 University Crescent
Winnipeg, Manitoba
R3T 2N6   CANADA

ABSTRACT

We studied the ecology of phytoplankton at eight sites in the Inuvik region of the Mackenzie Delta during 1985-86. Our study sites included a main channel of the river, lakes always connected to a main channel, and lakes connected to a main channel only during the spring flood. In situ photosynthesis was calculated from chlorophyll concentrations, photosynthesis parameters (P_m^B and α), and in situ water-transparency data; phytoplankton-nutrient status was assessed using a combination of physiological assays (N debt, P debt, alkaline-phosphatase activity) and chemical composition of particulates. Annual rates of photosynthesis were uniformly low (3.8 to 7.7 $g \cdot C \cdot m^{-2}$). Phytoplankton photosynthesis in the river channels and in lakes directly connected with river channels was always light-limited because of high turbidity. Phosphorus limitation was most severe late in the year in lakes that were farthest removed from river channels. Chrysophytes dominated at all stations but cryptomonads increased in abundance at light-limited stations; total phytoplankton biomass was similar everywhere.

COREGONID MIGRATIONS AND BROAD WHITEFISH STUDIES IN THE MACKENZIE DELTA REGION

K.T.J. Chang-Kue and E.F. Jessop

Department of Fisheries and Oceans
Freshwater Institute
501 University Crescent
Winnipeg, Manitoba
R3T 2N6   CANADA

ABSTRACT

The Mackenzie Delta fish community is not restricted to habitats within the Delta despite the variety of lake, channel and estuarine waters. A large component of the complex of anadromous coregonid species uses the main Delta as a migratory corridor to distant spawning, overwintering and summer habitats. Relative fish abundance in the Delta is influenced by the distinct migration patterns of these species.

Broad whitefish, the most valued species in the region, was the focal point of several studies. Because only large mature fish on spawning migrations were found in delta channels in the earliest surveys (1971 to 1976), the juvenile and immature fish were thought to inhabit delta lakes and coastal waters. While the presence of coregonids in coastal waters was not unexpected, the intensive use of nursery, foraging and overwintering habitats in lakes of coastal freshwater drainages by young-of-year, yearling, immature and sub-adult broad whitefish was a significant discovery in 1978 to 1979. Immature lake whitefish and least cisco also used these systems to a lesser extent. The link between coastal and Mackenzie Delta broad whitefish was verified when tagged immature broad whitefish from one of the Tuktoyaktuk Peninsula drainages, Kukjuktuk Creek, were recaptured in subsequent years as spawning migrants in the Mackenzie Delta.

The opportunity to expand the scope of field studies over a 12-year period was a key factor in obtaining the sequence of data that revealed how discrete age groups of anadromous coregonids used critical freshwater habitats located both within and outside the Delta. The specific migration behaviour of each group and the migration corridors linking these habitats constitute important components in both reproductive and non-reproductive life-history stages. As a result of these cumulative study efforts, the implications of proposed industrial developments on Mackenzie Delta migratory whitefish have become more perceptible.

INTRODUCTION

The Department of Fisheries and Oceans (DFO) has been involved in several projects aimed at expanding our knowledge on the fish community in the Mackenzie Delta. The Delta's immense size and profusion of lake and channel habitats usually impede the collection of adequate data to satisfy this objective in a short time period. Several DFO field studies, prompted by hydrocarbon exploration activities in 1971 to 1982, revealed important life history aspects of the five species of the whitefish family (Coregonidae) that inhabit the Mackenzie Delta: *Coregonus nasus* (broad whitefish), *C. clupeaformis* complex (lake whitefish), *C. autumnalis*, (Arctic cisco), *C. sardinella* complex (least cisco), and *Stenodus leucichthys* (inconnu).

Between 1971 and 1975, basic information on distribution, relative abundance and biological parameters such as length, weight, age, sexual maturity and feeding habits for the prominent fish species were obtained (Hatfield *et al.*, 1972a, 1972b; Stein *et al.*, 1973a, 1973b; Dryden *et al.*, 1973; Jessop *et al.*, 1974; Jessop and Lilley, 1975; Percy, 1975). These studies also documented the general extent and timing of coregonid fish migrating through the Mackenzie Delta on their way to upstream spawning areas.

A second series of studies, commencing in 1978, focused on the coastal area of the outer Mackenzie Delta and the Tuktoyaktuk Peninsula (Figure 1). As expected, coastal populations of coregonids were found in the nearshore waters of the Beaufort Sea. Significant numbers of broad whitefish, lake whitefish and least cisco also entered coastal drainages on the Tuktoyaktuk Peninsula to reach tundra lake habitats for feeding and overwintering (Bond and Erickson, 1982, 1985; Lawrence *et al.*, 1984; Chang-Kue and Jessop, 1991a). Other studies in Tuktoyaktuk Harbour expanded our knowledge of coastal fish populations (Bond, 1982; Hopky and Ratynski, 1983; Ratynski, 1983; Ratynski and de March, 1989). Tagging studies provided data on general overwintering and spawning destinations of fish from coastal streams (Chang-Kue and Jessop, 1991a). Reist and Bond (1988) provided the most recent review of the life histories of coregonids in the lower Mackenzie River.

This background paper presents a summary of the Delta's fish community, focusing on the spatial and temporal abundance of migratory coregonids during the ice-free period. In addition, selected broad whitefish data from the aforementioned studies are presented to indicate how migrations to and from distant freshwater habitats play an essential part in the life-history strategy, not only of the spawning adults, but also of other critical life-history stages of this whitefish species.

GENERAL METHODS

Fish were collected by DFO in the lower Mackenzie River and Mackenzie Delta during 1971 to 1975 with 137-m survey gillnet gangs comprised of six panels graded in mesh size (19 to 70 mm bar mesh). During 1980 to 1981, shorter 60-m and 35-m

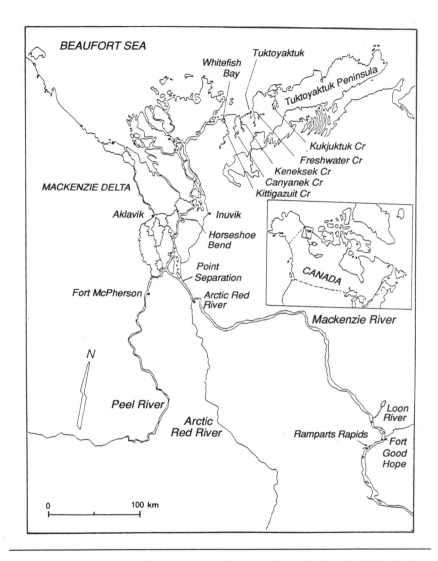

Figure 1. The lower Mackenzie River, Mackenzie Delta and Tuktoyaktuk Peninsula study area.

gangs were used (10 to 70 mm bar mesh). Beach seines were used to collect juveniles and other small fish during both survey periods in the Delta. General movements of coregonids were determined with a tag and recovery program. Fish

Chang-Kue and Jessop

were enumerated in a representative coastal stream, Kukjuktuk Creek, on the Tuktoyaktuk Peninsula where upstream and downstream runs were monitored simultaneously with a counting weir in 1978 to 1979 (Figure 1). Subsamples were taken for biological sampling while numerous broad whitefish also were tagged and released to study movements and migrations.

DELTA FISH COMMUNITY

Thirty-two freshwater and anadromous fish species have been recorded in the Mackenzie Delta (McCart, 1986) although 20 to 24 species are most commonly encountered in fish inventory programs. The composition of the fish fauna usually reflects the relative emphasis given to capture methods, sampling sites and sampling schedules. Some species, like the yellow walleye, are rarely seen because the Delta is at the northernmost fringe of their distribution. Other species may be limited to specific sites in the Delta. The arctic char, for example, is found in two streams flowing into the west side of the Delta and is usually taken in west delta channels during their migrations to and from the coast.

The twenty fish species taken in gillnets and beach seines during a 1980 survey in the northeast delta area included the most common species encountered in primary channel sites (Chang-Kue and Jessop, 1991b). The gillnet-catch data showed that broad whitefish, lake whitefish, arctic cisco, least cisco and inconnu comprised 79% of the catch (Table 1). Northern pike and burbot, the two primary predator species, comprised only 14.6% of the total catch. Had secondary channels been given equal sampling effort, less coregonid fish would have been taken and catches would have shown a greater proportion of predator species, especially the northern pike, which prefer such shallow, backwater habitats. Stray specimens of arctic grayling, lake trout, walleye, flathead chub and migratory chum salmon were also taken. Species most prevalent in beach seine catches were trout perch (25.3%), spoonhead sculpin (18.3%) and rainbow smelt (16.3%). Small coregonids collectively comprised 22.1% of the total beach seine catch.

Delta lakes show a different assemblage of fish because predator species concentrate in these areas to feed on a variety of juvenile coregonids that have entered the lakes during the annual spring floods. A survey in the spring of 1973 in a delta lake connected to Jamieson Channel (a no-closure type lake) indicated that the lake contained 43% pike, 0.3% burbot and 56.7% coregonids (unpublished data). More recently, Taylor *et al.* (1982) operated counting weirs in access channels to study the fish fauna in three representative no-closure delta lakes. They estimated that the population of larger fish (> 150 mm fork length), based on migrants leaving the lakes at freeze-up, was comprised of 44.7% burbot, 19.0% pike and 36.3% juvenile and immature coregonids.

Broad whitefish is the main migratory fish species taken in the region's subsistence fishery. Other species include inconnu, arctic char and burbot (Jessop *et al.*, 1974). Preference may vary according to region, seasonal availability and abundance. The other coregonid species are taken mainly for dog food. Broad whitefish have been the target of sporadic commercial fishing efforts; however, the viability of each attempt has been impeded by distribution and transportation costs. Corkum and McCart (1981) provided an historical review of the commercial and subsistence fishery of the area. McCart (1986) examined a variety of unpublished research and survey data for his review of fish and fisheries in the Mackenzie system.

COREGONID MIGRATIONS

All five coregonid species have been described as anadromous because of their movement into coastal waters for part of their life history. The degree of anadromy varies among these species and their ability to inhabit brackish waters for prolonged periods reflects their general distribution in

Table 1. Total catch of fish taken in survey gillnets and beach seines in the Northeast Mackenzie Delta, 1980.

SPECIES	GILLNET N	GILLNET %	BEACH SEINE N	BEACH SEINE %
Lake Whitefish	428	28.9	372	7.2
Broad Whitefish	367	24.8	0	--
Arctic Cisco	185	12.5	204	4.0
Least Cisco	127	8.6	481	9.4
Inconnu	62	4.2	51	1.0
Northern Pike	195	13.2	23	0.5
Burbot	21	1.4	187	3.7
Rainbow Smelt	27	1.8	832	16.3
Longnose Sucker	44	3.0	436	8.6
Arctic Grayling	2		0	
Chum Salmon	1		0	
Lake Trout	1	0.4	0	--
Walleye	1		0	
Flathead Chub	1		0	
Trout Perch	18	1.2	1289	25.3
Spoonhead Sculpin	0		938	18.3
Pond Smelt	0		125	2.5
Lake Chub	0	--	39	0.8
Ninespine Stickleback	0		82	1.6
Arctic Lamprey	0		18	0.4
Unidentified Whitefish	0		18	0.4
Total	1480	(100.0)	5095	(100.0)

nearshore or offshore environments (Craig and McCart, 1976; Lawrence et al., 1984). Arctic cisco is considered to be the most saline tolerant in the group followed by least cisco, broad whitefish, lake whitefish and inconnu (Craig, 1984). Mature spawning individuals of all five species migrate annually through the Delta towards a number of known or suspected spawning grounds in the main stem of the lower Mackenzie River. The capture of spawning migrants also indicated the presence of important spawning sites in major tributaries, especially the Peel River and Arctic Red River (Jessop et al., 1974). Few immature or non-spawning

Chang-Kue and Jessop

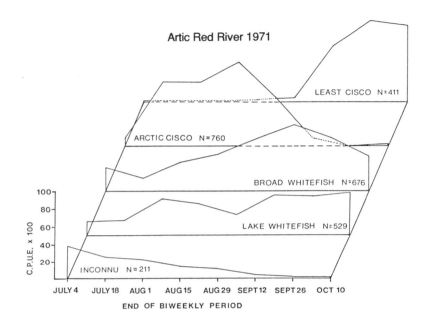

Figure 2. Biweekly catch-per-unit-of-effort for migratory coregonids in the Arctic Red River area, 1971.

coregonids participate in the major runs through the main body of the Mackenzie Delta (Chang-Kue and Jessop, 1991b). Spawning occurs from late-August to mid-November and specific times for each species vary with the wide spatial distribution of spawning sites in this large river system.

Differences in migration timing and migration rate through the primary delta channels by each species affects relative fish abundance on a spatial and temporal basis. The variation in coregonid abundance through the summer and fall was first documented in 1971 by Hatfield *et al.* (1972b). A summary of their biweekly catch-per-unit of effort data (number of fish per 100 yards of survey gillnet per hour) for each coregonid species is shown in Figure 2. This figure depicts the passage of discrete groups of spawning migrants through the Arctic Red River and upper Delta area. The pattern is consistent each year and occurs a week or two earlier in the middle Delta (Stein *et al.*, 1973a; Percy, 1975; Chang-Kue and Jessop, 1991b).

The inconnu is the first coregonid species to migrate through the Delta, beginning soon after break-up and reaching a peak in early-July at Arctic Red River

(Figure 2). The catch diminishes gradually over the summer as the pre-spawning fish proceed further upstream to spawning sites in major rivers such as the Peel and Arctic Red Rivers (Stein *et al.,* 1973b) and as far as the lower Liard River (McLeod *et al.*, 1979). Arctic cisco also begin their migrations early, as indicated by the appearance of discrete schools of cisco in delta channels in mid-July with catches peaking in August (Figure 2). The steep decline in numbers in September reflects their movement out of the area to upstream sites. Spawning occurs in major tributaries like the Peel, Arctic Red, Mountain (Jessop *et al.*, 1974), Great Bear (Chang-Kue and Cameron, 1980; McCart, 1982) and Liard Rivers (McLeod and O'Neil, 1983).

Both mature and immature lake whitefish begin to appear in greater numbers in the lower Delta in late-July or early-August. By September only immature and non-spawning adults are left because spawners have moved on into the upper Delta, the main stem Mackenzie, or major tributaries (Chang-Kue and Jessop, 1991b). Catches at Arctic Red River (Figure 2) reflect the arrival and continual passage of these spawners, some of which are believed to spawn near the confluence of this major tributary in mid-October (Dryden *et al.*, 1973). Several other main stem spawning areas are believed to exist at least as far upstream as the Ramparts Rapids.

Broad whitefish appear in increasing numbers by late-July in the lower Delta with fish numbers peaking in August (Chang-Kue and Jessop, 1991b), 2 to 3 weeks before the peak catches at Arctic Red River in mid-September (Figure 2). Mature broad whitefish hold and maintain in pre-spawning aggregations at several major eddies before spawning. Two known aggregation sites are Horseshoe Bend (in the Middle Channel) and the Loon River confluence, located downstream of Fort Good Hope (Figure 1). Broad whitefish may hold in such sites for 4 to 6 weeks prior to making a final upstream run at freeze-up (early-November) to major main-stem spawning sites at the Arctic Red River confluence, Point Separation and the Ramparts Rapids (Chang-Kue and Jessop, 1983). Other major spawning runs also occur in the Peel River and Arctic Red River (Stein *et al.*, 1973b).

Least cisco catches were the lowest among all the coregonid species throughout the summer; however, a major influx of cisco occurs by late-August in the lower reaches of the Middle and East channels (Percy, 1975; Chang-Kue and Jessop, 1991b). This least cisco run, following the peak and decline of the arctic cisco run, also was observed in the Delta by Stein *et al.* (1973b). Like the lake whitefish, both mature and immature fish comprised the run into the lower Delta; however, only mature spawners continued into the lower Mackenzie River (Figure 2). No spawning sites have been identified although the presence of mature least cisco in the Peel River (Stein *et al.*, 1973b) and in some of the Delta's west side channels (Jessop *et al.*, 1974) indicated potential spawning sites.

Downstream migrations of coregonids occur soon after spawning. Stein *et al.* (1973b) reported that spent, emaciated arctic cisco, examined at Aklavik in late-October 1972, comprised a major post-spawning run returning to estuarine areas. Anecdotal accounts by residents at Arctic Red River, Fort McPherson, Aklavik, and

Chang-Kue and Jessop

Inuvik describe similar under-ice return migrations occurring through the Delta as fish move to overwintering areas in the outer Delta and deep sections of main channels. After spawning near Point Separation during freeze-up in the first week of November 1984, radio-tagged broad whitefish showed that their post-spawning migration to outer delta sites was completed within 2 to 3 weeks (unpublished data).

BROAD WHITEFISH IN THE DELTA

The broad whitefish is the most important fish to delta residents by virtue of its availability, size and food quality. Migrants may be as old as 15 years and reach 665-mm fork length in size (Hatfield et al., 1972a). Broad whitefish as old as 22 years and as large as 798-mm fork length have been reported from lakes adjacent to Ya-Ya Lake on Richard's Island (Machniak, 1977). The most prominent observation made during 1971 to 1974 was the relative absence of young-of-year and immature broad whitefish in the Mackenzie Delta. In 1972, 95.4% of 911 broad whitefish taken in survey gillnets by Stein et al. (1973b) throughout the Delta and Arctic Red River were greater than 200-mm fork length (an approximate division between 1 and 2 year old broad whitefish). The length frequency distribution of this group of broad whitefish (>200 mm fork length) was skewed towards large fish (440 to 560 mm fork length) comprising 73.6% of the sample (Figure 3). Because the minimum size of spawners is approximately 400 to 430 mm fork length (age 6 to 8 years), this length distribution verified the predominance of only large, mature adults in the Mackenzie Delta broad whitefish catches.

Broad whitefish smaller than 200-mm fork length were seldom caught in gillnets, contributing only 4.6% of the total catch taken in 1972. Beach seining in the main channels in 1972 confirmed that broad whitefish fry and small juveniles were scarce in comparison to the other coregonid species (Stein et al., 1973b). Percy (1975) found that broad whitefish smaller than 200 mm comprised less than 2% of his total sample of broad whitefish in the outer delta channels and estuarine waters. It was thus apparent that main delta channels were not the primary habitats for young-of-year, yearlings and immature broad whitefish. The tentative conclusion reached by 1976 was that these early life-history stages inhabited numerous delta lakes and secondary channels that had not received the same level of sampling effort (Stein et al., 1973a, 1973b; Jessop et al., 1974).

BROAD WHITEFISH IN COASTAL DRAINAGES

Surveys in the outer Delta (Percy, 1975) and in coastal nearshore waters of Richards Island and Tuktoyaktuk Peninsula (Lawrence et al., 1984) established the major presence of anadromous coregonids. The two-year counting weir operation at Kukjuktuk Creek also revealed that this representative coastal stream provided a major migration corridor between its network of headwater lakes and the southern Beaufort coastal waters for three of the whitefish species (Chang-Kue and Jessop, 1991a). The migrations revealed a pattern of tundra lake habitat utilization by broad

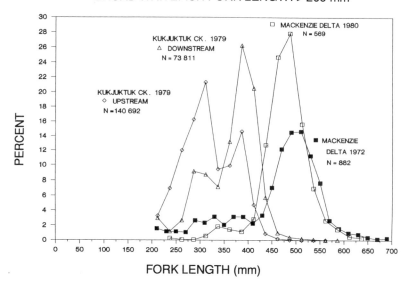

BROAD WHITEFISH FORK LENGTH > 200 mm

Figure 3. Length frequency distribution for broad whitefish (> 200 mm fork length) in the Mackenzie Delta (1972 and 1980) and at Kukjuktuk Creek in 1979.

whitefish, lake whitefish and least cisco that was more varied and complex than previously realized. Each species followed its own specific migration timing and activity level. In general, there was a complex pattern of both upstream and downstream movement involving groups, by decreasing age class, of migrating immature fish. Upstream runs began as soon as stream flows commenced; downstream runs began 2 to 3 weeks later. In 1979, when the stream was monitored from ice-out to freeze-up (June 13 to October 2), a total of 1,190,972 and 112,038 fish were enumerated in the upstream and downstream runs respectively (Table 2). Broad whitefish was the dominant species, comprising 96.4% of the total upstream and downstream count.

The most conspicuous observation made at Kukjuktuk Creek in 1979, when the counting weir was modified to capture small fish, was the predominance of broad whitefish in the 1 to 200 mm length group (Figure 4). These fish, comprising 88% of the total upstream run, were mainly young-of-year (26 to 75 mm fork length) and one-year-old fish (76 to 200 mm fork length) which appeared in the stream by mid-

Chang-Kue and Jessop

Table 2. Summary of fish enumerated at Kukjuktuk Creek, Tuktoyaktuk Peninsula in 1978 and 1979.

SPECIES	NUMBER OF FISH			
	1978		1979	
	Upstream	Downstream	Upstream	Downstream
Broad Whitefish	65,209	23,291	<200 mm f. length 1,029,662	11,668
			>200 mm f. length 140,692	73,811
Lake Whitefish	7,070	3,476	6,577	9,394
Least Cisco	14,102	6,951	14,037	17,168
Starry Flounder	1	2	3	0
Northern Pike	0	0	0	1
Arctic Char	0	0	1	0
Ninespine Stickleback	0	0	0	a
Pond Smelt	0	0	0	a
Rainbow Smelt	1	0	0	0
Fourhorn Sculpin	1	0	0	0

a = *Schools of migrants too numerous to count*

July and dominated the upstream run until late-August (Figure 4). The young-of-year originated from spawning grounds in the Mackenzie River while the yearlings most likely had spent their first summer and winter in Mackenzie Delta lakes. The upstream migration timing of these significant numbers and their relatively small proportion (1.1%) in the total run of fish returning to the coast by freeze-up indicated that the tundra lake system provided significant nursery and overwintering habitat for young-of-year and yearlings from the Mackenzie River.

No similar activity for fry and juveniles of the other coregonid species were observed during the 1979 fish counts. Fish in the 1 to 200 mm length group comprised only 1.4% and 2.0% of the total upstream run of lake whitefish (N=6,577) and least cisco (N=14,037) respectively (Chang-Kue and Jessop, 1991a).

The young-of-year broad whitefish reside in the lakes for up to 4 years before joining a group of immature fish (age 4 to 8 years) that undertake annual migrations between the coastal zone and the tundra lakes. These immature downstream migrants overwinter in deep coastal bays or outer delta waters before returning to Kukjuktuk Creek or adjacent coastal drainages the next spring for summer feeding in the lakes (Chang-Kue and Jessop, 1991a). Tagging data also showed that some of these broad whitefish, after a summer of feeding, may forego the annual return to coastal waters and use the lakes as alternate overwintering sites. The numbers involved may be significant since only 30% of broad whitefish upstream migrants

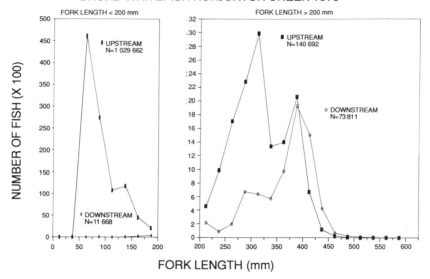

BROAD WHITEFISH KUKJUKTUK CREEK 1979

Figure 4. Length frequency distribution for all broad whitefish in the upstream and downstream migrations at Kukjuktuk Creek, 1979.

in the 200 to 375 mm size range returned downstream in 1979 (Figure 4). Year-to-year variability in the size of upstream versus downstream runs may occur since the complex migration and residency patterns may be influenced by run-off, stream flow and local climatic conditions. A comparison between 1978 and 1979 data was not possible because an intermittent fish counting schedule and interruptions due to flooding by coastal storms limited the accuracy of the daily fish counts in 1978.

The overall length frequency distribution in Figure 4 also showed that broad whitefish in the 200 to 450 mm range were dominant among the older (>200 mm fork length) Kukjuktuk Creek migrants, comprising 99.8% of the upstream run and 98.4% of the downstream run. These fish corresponded to the part of the length distribution not seen in the Delta. A comparison of the broad whitefish length frequencies in the Mackenzie Delta (1972) with the length frequencies at Kukjuktuk Creek showed that the distributions complemented each other (Figure 3). We concluded that coastal freshwater drainages, located outside the Delta, provided major habitats for the immature members of the Mackenzie River broad whitefish.

Chang-Kue and Jessop

A more recent survey in the East Channel region of the Mackenzie Delta in 1980 provided another set of data for comparison of length frequencies between delta and coastal whitefish (Chang-Kue and Jessop, 1991b). The length frequency distribution of the 1980 delta sample (N=569) was similar to the 1972 sample in terms of its distinct skewness towards the large size classes of broad whitefish (Figure 3). Extensive sampling effort in 1980 with beach seines and smaller mesh survey gillnets confirmed also that broad whitefish fry and juveniles were essentially absent in the delta channels although juveniles of the other four coregonids were encountered (Table 1). This consistency of unique length distribution pattern by region verified our conclusion that the majority of broad whitefish found in the Mackenzie Delta channels were mature or pre-spawning adult fish while a significant portion of the young-of-year, juveniles, immatures and sub-adults not only inhabited nearshore coastal areas, but also inhabited suitable coastal freshwater drainages flowing into the southern Beaufort Sea.

The earliest downstream migrants at Kukjuktuk Creek included large fish that had not been counted among the earlier upstream migrants; these were presumed to be mature fish foregoing another summer of lake foraging to begin their migration to spawning areas (Chang-Kue and Jessop, 1991a). Some of these fish may have been lake resident for one or more years prior to reaching maturity. Gonad maturity analysis by Bond and Erickson (1985) on broad whitefish from Freshwater Creek, another coastal system, showed that some of the earliest migrants to leave that stream were large, mature fish that would spawn in the fall. The final link between coastal and delta populations was provided when Kukjuktuk Creek broad whitefish, tagged and released as immature fish in 1978-1979, were recaptured at Arctic Red River, Fort Good Hope and several Mackenzie Delta sites in subsequent years. These fish were 8 years and older at the time of recapture and were consistent with the known age of spawning adults (Chang-Kue and Jessop, 1991a).

MIGRATION AND LIFE-HISTORY STRATEGY

Anadromous fish migrate between freshwater and coastal habitats. Spawned and reared for one or more seasons in the freshwater streams, these fish enter coastal areas to feed in the summer and return to estuaries, streams and lakes to overwinter or to spawn when mature. While fish studies in the Delta improved our life-history knowledge of the anadromous coregonids, the significant role of other freshwater drainages reached through a nearshore corridor was only revealed by the opportunity to expand the scope of our studies with time. The accumulated knowledge demonstrated that migratory behaviour also was an important strategy for the early non-reproductive life-history stages of this species.

While the role of Mackenzie Delta lakes as nursery and foraging habitats for fry and immature fish is still considered important, we now realize that the coastal drainages with their network of tundra lakes provide significant alternatives. Kukjuktuk Creek is just one of several similar drainages supporting fish on the Tuktoyaktuk Peninsula and Richards Island (Bond and Erickson, 1982, 1985;

Lawrence *et al.*, 1984). One major factor facilitating coastal migrations is the significant input of freshwater into the Beaufort Sea by the Mackenzie River. There is a freshwater plume extending up the coast to McKinley Bay as a result of interaction with cold saline water, prevailing winds and the earth's rotational Coriolis effect. This situation provides an extended coastal freshwater environment along the nearshore zone for the low-salinity tolerant species such as the broad whitefish and lake whitefish.

Migratory ability and accessibility of distant habitats provide important advantages to the broad whitefish population. Access to the networks of lakes on Tuktoyaktuk Peninsula significantly increases the area of feeding habitats. For the fry and small juvenile broad whitefish, competition with other coregonid species like the lake whitefish and least cisco is minimized by their greater ability to inhabit tundra lakes within their first two years. Major nursery areas for the lake whitefish and least cisco are located in the Mackenzie Delta and adjacent coastal areas (Chang-Kue and Jessop, 1991b; Bond and Erickson, 1985).

The water quality of Tuktoyaktuk Peninsula lakes would seem to offer an advantage over delta lakes as prime habitat for the broad whitefish fry and yearlings. However, a recent two-year study comparing several delta and tundra lakes found that differences in phytoplankton productivity alone were not significant enough to support this speculation (Fee *et al.*, 1988). On the other hand, Tuktoyaktuk Peninsula lakes are not subject to occasional summer flood events; therefore, the stable summer conditions for zooplankton and benthic production may be more suitable for optimum feeding over the short summer by the youngest and smallest planktivorous whitefish as well as the older, benthivorous whitefish. The specific aspects of fish behaviour, trophic pathways, and long-term comparison between the two types of lakes still require further study.

Overwintering habitats in the deeper lakes of the Tuktoyaktuk Peninsula provide an opportunity for optimum growth during the early years (0 to 4 years) because no energy would be expended in annual long-distance migrations. The presence of deep overwintering lakes adjacent to shallow foraging lakes is an advantage as summer feeding time is maximized. These same lakes also appear to provide alternate overwintering areas for the particular group of older juveniles and sub-adults that overwinter in the lakes instead of returning annually to coastal overwintering sites (Chang-Kue and Jessop, 1991b). Such partitioning of the population over several sites ensures a better chance of survival over the winter particularly if a catastrophic event should decimate fish in one area.

The lack of predators in key habitats would ensure better survival for juvenile and immature coregonids. Although tundra lakes do harbour predators such as burbot and northern pike (Lawrence *et al.*, 1984), their population densities are considered to be less than those in the delta lakes and secondary channels where northern pike is especially abundant. Taylor *et al.* (1982) believed that these two predator species may be the major limiting factor to the production of small coregonids in Mackenzie Delta lakes. They estimated that pike consumed from four

Chang-Kue and Jessop

to 54 times more fish biomass than what actually escaped into the main delta channels from their delta study lakes by the end of the summer. More predation occurs in the late-fall as large aggregations of burbot and northern pike can be found at discrete channel sites feeding on juvenile fish emerging from the outflow of shallow lakes at freeze-up.

VULNERABILITY TO IMPACTS

While migratory behaviour may impart advantages to coastal coregonid populations, the narrow migration corridors linking these specific habitats may in turn make the broad whitefish population more susceptible to potential adverse effects of proposed industrial developments. Passage along the nearshore zone may be delayed by shoreline structures and offshore activities associated with hydrocarbon development. Kukjuktuk Creek itself is particularly vulnerable; any blockage of this small, seemingly minor tundra stream by improper road or pipeline crossings may disrupt several life-history stages because no alternate access route to headwater lake habitats is available. The routing of such linear facilities across the Delta and along Tuktoyaktuk Peninsula to McKinley Bay may exacerbate potential impacts since several similar coastal drainages will have to be crossed.

On a larger scale, the reduction of flow or alteration of timing of the Mackenzie River discharge as a result of a major or cumulative series of hydroelectric developments in the upper Mackenzie drainage may disrupt the present characteristics of the coastal migration corridor. Changes in the freshwater input to the Beaufort Sea could limit access along the nearshore coastal corridor, reduce the opportunities to use critical coastal drainages, and ultimately result in negative impacts on Mackenzie Delta fish populations.

There is still a significant lack of data on various stocks or populations of each coregonid species. Each spawning stock may demonstrate unique life-history variations in terms of their use of regional critical habitats and specific migration behaviour. Without this information, management of the Mackenzie Delta's complex of coregonid populations cannot be accomplished effectively (Reist and Bond, 1988).

SUMMARY

The Mackenzie Delta's vast network of lakes and channels supports a large assemblage of fish species. The most prominent species among the 32 recorded include the broad whitefish, lake whitefish, arctic cisco, least cisco and inconnu. Significant spawning migrations of these anadromous coregonids occur through major delta channels each year. Since the migration pattern of each species differ, relative fish abundance data reflect the temporal and spatial factors associated with migrations as well as fishing effort.

The most valued species in the region's subsistence fishery is the broad whitefish. Data prior to 1978 showed that broad whitefish size distribution in the Delta was skewed toward fish larger than 400-mm fork length, representing the mature segment of the population. The virtual absence of young-of-year fish and a scarcity of immature fish in main delta channels led to an initial conclusion that their principal habitats were delta lakes and coastal areas respectively.

Subsequent work in the adjacent Beaufort Sea coastal region studied coastal coregonid populations and documented the significant use of freshwater drainages on Tuktoyaktuk Peninsula and Richards Island by broad whitefish. A small tundra creek usually provided the single access to major nursery and overwintering habitats in the network of tundra lakes in its headwaters. Migrations within a creek were quite complex and reflected specific behaviour patterns related to: residency by young-of-year, annual migrations by immature fish between coastal waters and lake foraging sites, and alternate residency in lakes by other immature fish. Immature broad whitefish tagged in Kukjuktuk Creek were recaptured in subsequent years as spawning migrants in the Mackenzie River, thereby verifying the link between delta and coastal broad whitefish.

Our understanding of habitat use by discrete life-history stages of broad whitefish in different regions was obtained only after data was accumulated from a series of studies that were given the opportunity to expand and evolve in scope over 12 years. Similar detail on the other four coregonids is still required. Additional studies on coastal fish populations, especially arctic cisco, are being conducted (Bond and Erickson, 1987, 1989) and further research efforts need to be directed at determining specific life-history characteristics of individual spawning stocks so that effective habitat protection and management of the region's migratory coregonid populations can be accomplished.

REFERENCES

BOND, W.A., 1982. A study of the fishery resources of Tuktoyaktuk Harbour, southern Beaufort Sea coast, with special reference to life histories of anadromous coregonids. Canadian Technical Report of Fisheries and Aquatic Sciences No.1119, Fisheries and Oceans Canada, 90 pp.

BOND, W.A. and R.N. ERICKSON, 1982. Preliminary results of a fisheries study of two freshwater lake systems on the Tuktoyaktuk Peninsula, Northwest Territories. Canadian Data Report on Fisheries and Aquatic Sciences No.348, Fisheries and Oceans Canada, 62 pp.

BOND, W.A. and R.N. ERICKSON, 1985. Life history studies of anadromous coregonid fishes in two freshwater lake systems on the Tuktoyaktuk Peninsula, Northwest Territories. Canadian Technical Report of Fisheries and Aquatic Sciences No.1336, Western Region, Fisheries and Oceans Canada, Winnipeg, Manitoba, 61 pp.

BOND, W.A. and R.N. ERICKSON, 1987. Fishery data from Phillips Bay, Yukon, 1985. Canadian Data Report on Fisheries and Aquatic Sciences No.635, Fisheries and Oceans Canada, 39 pp.

BOND, W.A. and R.N. ERICKSON, 1989. Summer studies of the nearshore fish community at Phillips Bay, Beaufort Sea coast, Yukon. Canadian Technical Report of Fisheries and Aquatic Sciences No.1676, Fisheries and Oceans Canada, 102 pp.

CHANG-KUE, K.T.J. and R.A. CAMERON, 1980. A survey of the fish resources of the Great Bear River, Northwest Territories, 1974. Manuscript Report No.1510, Canadian Fisheries and Marine Service, 59 pp.

CHANG-KUE, K.T.J. and E.F. JESSOP, 1983. Tracking the movements of adult broad whitefish (*Coregonus nasus*) to their spawning grounds in the Mackenzie River, Northwest Territories. Proceedings, 4th International Conference on Wildlife Biotelemetry, D.G. Pincock (Editor), 22-24 August 1983. Halifax, Nova Scotia, 248-266

CHANG-KUE, K.T.J. and E.F. JESSOP, 1991a. Coregonid migration studies at Kukjuktuk Creek, a major freshwater drainage on the Tuktoyaktuk Peninsula, Northwest Territories. Canadian Technical Report of Fisheries and Aquatic Sciences, Fisheries and Oceans Canada, (under review)

CHANG-KUE, K.T.J. and E.F. JESSOP, 1991b. Fish resource data from the northeast and upper section of the Mackenzie Delta, 1980-1981. Canadian Manuscript Report of Fisheries and Aquatic Sciences, Fisheries and Oceans Canada, (under review)

CORKUM, L.D. and P.J. McCART, 1981. A review of the fisheries the Mackenzie Delta and nearshore Beaufort Sea. Canadian Manuscript Report of Fisheries and Aquatic Sciences No.1613, Fisheries and Oceans Canada, 55 pp.

CRAIG, P.C., 1984. Fish use of coastal waters of the Alaskan Beaufort Sea: a review. Transactions of the American Fisheries Society, 113(3), 265-282

CRAIG, P.C., and P. McCART, 1976. Fish use of nearshore coastal waters in the western Arctic: emphasis on anadromous species. In - Assessment of the Arctic Marine Environment: Selected Topics, D.W. Hood and D.C. Burnell (Editors), Occasional Publication No.4. Institute of Marine Science, University of Alaska, Fairbanks, Alaska, 361-388

DRYDEN, R.L., B.G. SUTHERLAND, and J.N. STEIN, 1973. An evaluation of the fish resources of the Mackenzie River valley as related to pipeline development: Volume II. Report No.73-2, Environmental-Social Committee, Northern Pipelines, Task Force on Northern Oil Development, Ottawa, Ontario, April, 176 pp.

FEE, E.J., R.E. HECKY, S.J. GUILDFORD, C. ANEMA, D. MATHEW, and K. HALLARD, 1988. Phytoplankton primary production and related limnological data for lakes and channels in the Mackenzie Delta and lakes on the Tuktoyaktuk Peninsula, N.W.T. Canadian Technical Report of Fisheries and Aquatic Sciences No.1614, Fisheries and Oceans Canada, Ottawa, Ontario, 62 pp.

HATFIELD, C.T., J.N. STEIN, M.R. FALK and C.S. JESSOP, 1972a. Fish resources of the Mackenzie River valley, Interim Report 1, Volume I. Fisheries Service, Environment Canada, Winnipeg, Manitoba, 247 pp.

HATFIELD, C.T., J.N. STEIN, M.R. FALK, C.S. JESSOP and D.N. SHEPHERD, 1972b. Fish resources of the Mackenzie River valley, Interim Report 1, Volume II. Fisheries Service, Environment Canada, Winnipeg, Manitoba, 289 pp.

HOPKY, G.E. and R.A. RATYNSKI, 1983. Relative abundance, spatial and temporal distribution, age and growth of fishes in Tuktoyaktuk Harbour, N.W.T. 28 June to 5 September 1981. Canadian Manuscript Report of Fisheries and Aquatic Sciences No.1713, Fisheries and Oceans Canada, 71 pp.

JESSOP, C.S., K.T.J. CHANG-KUE, J.W. LILLEY, and R.J. PERCY, 1974. A further evaluation of the fish resources of the Mackenzie River Valley as related to pipeline development. Report No.74-7, Environmental-Social Committee, Northern Pipelines, Task Force on Northern Oil Development, Ottawa, Ontario, June, 95 pp.

JESSOP, C.S. and J.W. LILLEY, 1975. An evaluation of the fish resources of the Mackenzie River based on 1974 data. Technical Report Series No.75-6, Resource Management Branch, Fisheries and Marine Service, Environment Canada, 97 pp.

LAWRENCE, M.J., G. LACHO, and S. DAVIES, 1984. A survey of the coastal fishes of the southeastern Beaufort Sea. Canadian Technical Report of Fisheries and Aquatic Sciences No.1220, Fisheries and Oceans Canada, 178 pp.

MACHNIAK, K., 1977. Investigations of the fisheries resources in lakes in the vicinity of the Ya-Ya gravel esker. Report by Aquatic Environments Limited for Department of Indian and Northern Affairs, Ottawa, Ontario, 105 pp.

McCART, D., 1982. An assessment of the fisheries resources of the Great Bear and Mackenzie rivers in the vicinity of proposed IPL pipeline crossings. Report by Aquatic Environments Limited, Calgary for Interprovincial Pipe Lines (N.W.) Ltd., Calgary, Alberta, 53 pp.

McCART, P.J., 1986. Fish and fisheries of the Mackenzie system. In - The Ecology of River Systems, B.R. Davies and K.F. Walker (Editors). Dr. W. Junk Publishers, Dordrecht, The Netherlands, 493-515

McLEOD, C., J. O'NEIL, L. HILDEBRAND, and T. CLAYTON, 1979. An examination of fish migrations in the Liard River, British Columbia, relative to proposed hydroelectric development at site A. Preliminary Report by RL & L Environmental Services Ltd., Edmonton for British Columbia Hydro and Power Authority, Vancouver, British Columbia, 1 volume

McLEOD, C.L., and J.P. O'NEIL, 1983. Major range extension of anadromous salmonids and first record of chinook salmon in the Mackenzie River drainage. Canadian Journal of Zoology, 61(9), 2183-2184

PERCY, R., 1975. Fishes of the outer Mackenzie Delta. Beaufort Sea Technical Report No.8, Beaufort Sea Project, Department of the Environment, Victoria, British Columbia, 114 pp.

RATYNSKI, R.A., 1983. Mid-summer ichthyoplankton populations of Tuktoyaktuk Harbour, N.W.T. Canadian Technical Report of Fisheries and Aquatic Sciences No.1218, Fisheries and Oceans Canada, 21 pp.

RATYNSKI, R.A., and B.G.E. de MARCH, 1989. Description of a developmental series of larval broad whitefish, *Coregonus nasus* (Pallas). Canadian Technical Report of Fisheries and Aquatic Sciences No.1670, Fisheries and Oceans Canada, 12 pp.

REIST, J.D., and W.A. BOND, 1988. Life history characteristics of migratory coregonids of the lower Mackenzie River, Northwest Territories, Canada. Finnish Fisheries Research, Vol.9, 133-144

STEIN, J.N., C.S. JESSOP, T.R. PORTER, and K.T.J. CHANG-KUE, 1973a. An evaluation of the fish resources of the Mackenzie River valley as related to pipeline development: Volume I. Report No.73-1, Environmental-Social Committee, Northern Pipelines, Task Force on Northern Oil Development, Ottawa, Ontario, April, 121 pp.

STEIN, J.N., C.S. JESSOP, T.R. PORTER, and K.T.J. CHANG-KUE, 1973b. Fish resources of the Mackenzie River valley: interim report II. Fisheries Service, Department of the Environment, Winnipeg, Manitoba, for the Environmental-Social Program, Northern Pipelines, Ottawa, Ontario, July, 260 pp.

TAYLOR, J., S. McCORMICK, K. ENGLISH, and A. SEKERAK, 1982. Fisheries and limnological studies in selected lakes in the Mackenzie Delta, 1981. Report by LGL Environmental Research Associates for British Columbia Hydro and Power Authority, Vancouver, British Columbia, 240 pp.

USE OF LANDSAT THEMATIC MAPPER AND MULTI-SPECTRAL SCANNING IMAGERY TO IDENTIFY HABITATS AND SHOREBIRD NESTING AREAS ON THE OUTER MACKENZIE RIVER DELTA, N.W.T.

H.L. Dickson[1] and A.R. Smith[2]

[1]Canadian Wildlife Service
Environment Canada
4999 - 98 Avenue, 2nd Floor
Edmonton, Alberta
T6B 2X3   CANADA

[2]Canadian Wildlife Service
Environment Canada
115 Perimeter Road
Saskatoon, Saskatchewan
S7N 0X4   CANADA

ABSTRACT

In 1985, we initiated a program to define and map shorebird nesting habitat in a 20,300 hectare area around Fish Island, Northwest Territories using LANDSAT imagery.   We examined both Multi-spectral Scanner (MSS) and Thematic Mapper (TM) imagery for their suitability in conducting this work.   Digital and visual analyses of TM imagery, in conjunction with ground field data were used.

Visual analysis alone was used to expand these findings to the remainder of the outer Mackenzie River Delta and Richards Island.   Over 350 sites were identified as potential nesting or staging habitat.   These sites will help management of future development proposals, land-use planners, and other researchers interested in habitat/wildlife correlations in the future.

INTRODUCTION

In response to the federal Northern Oil and Gas Action Program (NOGAP) to advance government preparedness in the north for hydrocarbon development, the Canadian Wildlife Service initiated a project in 1985 to define and map major shorebird nesting sites on the Mackenzie River Delta.

We undertook to define habitat types and the habitat requirements, distribution and abundance of shorebirds on the outer Mackenzie River Delta and then to evaluate and map these nest areas using LANDSAT imagery.   The study concentrates on four "priority species":   [1. hudsonian godwit, *Limosa haemastica* (Linnaeus); 2. whimbrel, *Numenius phaeopus* (Linnaeus); 3. stilt sandpiper, *Calidris himantopus* (Bonaparte); and 4. long-billed dowitcher, *Limnodromus scolo paceus* (Say)] although we collected data on all bird species found in the area.

METHOD

The study concentrated initially on a small area of the outer Mackenzie River Delta slated as the site for the Taglu gas-gathering system, henceforth referred to as the main study area. We applied the resulting techniques of this first study to the remainder of the outer Mackenzie River Delta (Figure 1). From 1985 through 1987 we surveyed a total of 32 transects throughout the main study area and a few outside of this area (Figure 2). On each transect, we recorded the species, number of individuals, location of each sighting and the bird(s) behaviour. Shorebird nests were mapped, eggs counted and weighed and revisited to define hatch time. We recorded bird data in relation to the habitat type in which it was sighted. The habitat variables we recorded and used to define the habitat included: aspect (upland, lowland or slope); relief features which involved recording the abundance and/or development of high-centred polygons, low-centred polygons, mounds (= 5 foot diameter and 1 to 3 feet high), tussocks (*Eriophorum*) and hummocks (= 1 foot diameter frost-heaved feature); soil moisture; percent cover of open water (lakes, streams, ponds or rivers); percent cover and depth of standing water over vegetation; and percent cover of vegetation on the land excluding the open-water areas and of a number of vegetation variables (graminoides (which includes sedges and grasses), tall shrubs, dwarf shrubs, moss and lichens, flowering herbs and Equisetum). We analyzed the data collected in 1985 to broadly define the habitat requirements of the "priority species" (whimbrel, hudsonian godwit, stilt sandpiper and long-billed dowitcher).

In 1986 and 1987 we collected data similar to those collected for transects on a grid system (200 x 200 m) set up on Fish Island (Figure 3), the area with the highest densities of shorebirds of all transects surveyed in 1985 (Figure 2). The grid system also enabled us to plot nest sites accurately and the movements of the parents around their nest.

Using the 1986 habitat data collected on the Fish Island grid area we produced base maps of the percent cover of graminoides, dwarf shrub, tall shrub and standing water at various depths. We also mapped the nest sites of the "priority species". We provided these base maps, the 1985 transect habitat and bird data, and aerial photographs taken from a helicopter flying at 100 feet, to Dennis Jaques of Ecosat Geobotanical Services who did the LANDSAT mapping aspect of the project.

One scene of LANDSAT Multi-spectral Scanner Imagery (MSSI) and two images of one scene of Thematic Mapper Imagery (TMI) representing a June 21 and a July 23, 1986 date were ordered for the main study area. The applicability of LANDSAT MSSI to TMI for the study was evaluated. Following preprocessing of the LANDSAT TMI (Jaques, 1987) we prepared and selected image (band) enhancement combinations that would allow differentiation of vegetation cover types, water bodies, and water regimes. Once selected, we conducted an Unsupervised Maximum Likelihood Classification Analysis, known as the Maximum Likelihood Decision Rule (Van Trees, 1968), of the Fish Island area, using the July 23, 1986 LANDSAT TMI. Two colour maps, illustrating the results of this analysis, were produced

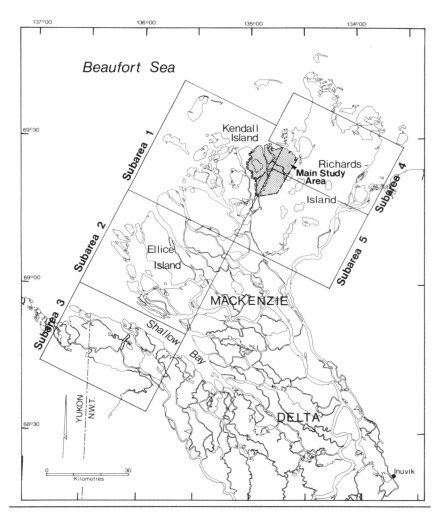

Figure 1. Study area location of the 1985 to 1987 shorebird project on the outer Mackenzie River Delta, Northwest Territories.

illustrating the different Land Classification Units (LCUs) on Fish Island. The actual habitats these LCUs represented were defined with the aid of the habitat field data collected in 1985 and 1986.

Nest data from 1985 (Figure 3) were then mapped onto the LCU maps. Further analyses and enhancements of the LCUs were conducted using the June and July TMI to further subdivide the LCUs which appeared most important to the

Dickson and Smith

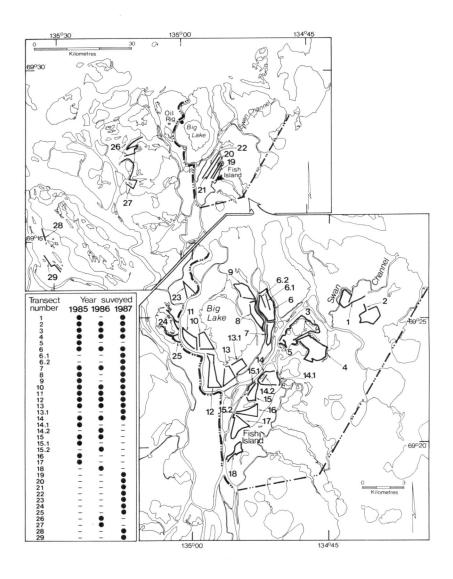

Figure 2. *Transect locations and year(s) each transect was surveyed on the Mackenzie River delta study area, 1985 to 1987.*

shorebirds. We utilized the resulting analyses in combination with the field habitat maps and the nest site maps to define and map priority nesting habitat in the Fish Island area. Visual interpretation using the June and July TMI was then utilized to define priority nesting areas throughout the main study area (Figure 1).

LANDSAT TMI scenes which covered the remainder of the outer Mackenzie River Delta (Figure 1) were acquired, and processed to produce visual enhancements. Using visual interpretation and comparison with preferred habitat on Fish Island, we identified and mapped priority nesting habitats for the area represented on these images.

We conducted a variety of statistical tests using field data from 1985 to 1987 to assess:

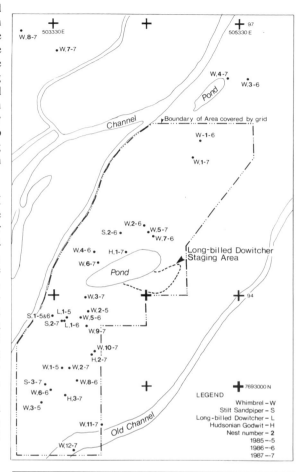

Figure 3. Shorebird nest sites and 200 x 200 m grid survey boundary locations on Fish Island and adjacent areas, Northwest Territories in 1985, 1986 and 1987.

1. If the areas defined as priority nesting habitat using the LANDSAT TMI analysis were actually used by shorebirds;
2. Which imagery (June or July) better defined the nesting areas;
3. If the species differentiated between habitat types and which habitats (LCUs) they preferred; and,
4. Which habitat variables were most important to the shorebirds in selecting the habitats they utilized, and if there was any apparent priority to those variables.

Dickson and Smith

RESULTS

Before defining where detailed grid surveys should be conducted and to guide the LANDSAT analyses we conducted a number of preliminary analyses of the 1985 data. Chi-square tests of the shorebird data and habitat data from 83.5 km of transects surveyed in 1985 (Figure 2) indicated that the priority species are most abundant in well-developed low-centred polygon habitat (chi-square = 4,550.52; df=4 p<0.01). We conducted this analysis after defining 7 broad habitat types: lowlands with well-developed or poorly-developed low-centred polygons; lowland levees; uplands with or without high-centred polygons; areas possessing tall shrubs; and barren areas (gravel pads, drift lines or mudflats).

The preference for low-centred polygons may be a function of the proximity of various habitat components required for nesting shorebirds such as dry areas for nesting and shallow waters for foraging. The better developed the polygons, the smaller the area within which these requirements can be met.

Examination of the 1985 bird data by transect indicates that those transects located on the southern half of Fish Island had the highest density of priority shorebirds of all transects surveyed.

The analysis of suitability of the June 21, 1986 LANDSAT MSSI was conducted in conjunction with the LANDSAT TMI. Since TMI, compared to MSSI, had higher spectral resolution, visual interpretation capabilities at much lower scales, more data bands for analysis and the capability to differentiate four times as many radiometric levels we selected TMI for the analysis. Readers are referred to Jaques (1987) for details on preprocessing of LANDSAT digital data and preparation and selection of photographic image-enhancement combinations used to differentiate the vegetation cover types.

Using a July 23 TMI for the main study area, evaluation of each major image-enhancement combination showed that numerous vegetation cover types could be differentiated. No single TM colour composite could be used to map all possible vegetation types. Three of the colour combinations were required to differentiate vegetation types, water-body types, water regimes and upland versus lowland habitat. These were the natural colour (bands 1-2-3), false colour infrared (2-3-4) and colour mid-infrared (3-4-5) images.

We used a June 21, 1986 TMI to differentiate water regimes on the main study area. Use of this image also enabled us to compare water-regime changes from periods shortly after the spring-flood peak and at the end of the shorebird nesting period. In 1985, we had established that shorebird nesting was initiated only upon drawdown of flood waters over outer delta lands following spring break-up.

Using an unsupervised Maximum Likelihood Classifier analysis (Van Trees, 1968) of the July 23, 1986 LANDSAT TMI of the Fish Island study area we generated vegetation cover maps of the study area at a scale of approximately 4 miles to the inch (i.e., 1:15,840). The maps illustrated 21 LANDSAT Classification Units (LCUs), or habitat types, as defined in Table 1. Only one map has been presented here (Figure 4). Habitat base maps, aerial slide coverage and nest site habitat data were used to define the LCUs.

We plotted nest data only for the priority shorebird species collected in 1985 (Figure 3) onto the LCU maps. All nests fell within LCU #9 (dark green on Figure 4).

Habitat data collected from actual nest sites showed that only portions of the habitat complex included in LCU #9 were selected for nest sites. LCU #9 was then subdivided by visual interpretation which allowed for the separation of much drier areas, in well-developed low-centred polygons without dense shrub cover (<55%) in LCU #9, on the basis of colour. Figure 5 shows the location of these prime potential nesting areas on Fish Island using the July imagery.

Field data also indicated that priority species were limited by the amount of standing water present on the land at nest initiation. Areas with 15 to 40% standing water on June 21 appeared to be selected as nesting areas. The June 21 imagery, Bands 3-4-5 enhanced photograph, was used to visually interpret and map the area on Fish Island falling within the 15 to 40% standing-water regime (Figure 5).

To define potential nesting habitat throughout the main study area, the June 21, 1986 LANDSAT TMI was produced for this area and visually interpreted for potential prime nesting habitat areas. (Funding levels did not allow for digital analyses of TMI throughout the main study area.) We also conducted visual interpretation of the natural colour, false-colour infrared and colour mid-infrared images for this larger area, to exclude areas of dense shrub cover and areas which did not dry sufficiently by July to serve as important nesting habitat.

Initial analyses and mapping of the June 21, 1986 LANDSAT TM enhanced image located 22 areas within the main study area which appear to be similar to the prime nesting habitat located on Fish Island. Subsequent refinement of that first stage of mapping with the three enhanced July TM images showed that only portions of those areas and, in fact, not all of them meet the other requirements as areas with potential nest sites (Figure 6 in part).

In 1987 we expanded mapping of priority nesting habitat throughout the outer Mackenzie Delta and Richards Island (Figure 1) using visual interpretation of July TMI. Figures 6, 7, 8 and 9 present the results of this evaluation.

We were able to test the results of the LANDSAT TMI mapping process in a number of ways using data collected from all three years. Nests of the priority species found on Fish Island (Figure 3) were plotted over the maps showing priority nesting habitat (Figure 5). The hudsonian godwit nests (3) all fell within the nesting area defined using the July TMI analysis. The long-billed dowitcher nest fell just outside (60 m) the priority area while stilt sandpipers were within the nesting zone 4 out of 5 times (1 was out by 60 m) using the July TMI analysis and one out of five

Table 1. Definition of each habitat type represented by pixel colours (LCU types) identified on Fish Island, Northwest Territories.

LCU#	COLOUR	FIGURE	HABITAT REPRESENTATION
1	Red	4	Water with heavy sediment concentration
2	Purple	4	Water with moderate sediment concentration
3	Tan	NA	Water with little suspended sediment
4	Tan	4	Shallow tundra ponds with little emergent vegetation
5	Lime Green	4	Largely covered by deep water with 10-15% vegetation cover in July
6	Reddish Brown	NA	About equal proportion of deep water and vegetation cover in late July
7	Orange	4	Wet sites covered by emergent vegetation: up to 15% deep water cover
8	Yellow	NA	>55% grass/sedge cover: 25-27 June with >75% standing water
9	Dark Green	4	Mixed dwarf shrub and grass/sedge: grass sedge >15%, dwarf shrub <35%
10	Dark Blue	4	>35% dwarf shrub represent gradient in dwarf shrub density and height from lowest to highest from LCU #10 to 12 respectively
11	Light Blue	4	>35% dwarf shrub represent gradient in dwarf shrub density and height from lowest to highest from LCU #10 to 12 respectively
12	Purple	NA	>35% dwarf shrub represent gradient in dwarf shrub density and height from lowest to highest from LCU #10 to 12 respectively
13	Grey	4	Dwarf shrub dominated Pleistocene upland
14	Lime Green	NA	Barren gravel with vegetation removed by human activity
15	Orange	NA	Unvegetated mudflats
16	Light Blue	NA	Disturbed sites with some grasses and herbs
17	Brown	NA	Disturbed sites: gravel with tall shrubs or exposed peat
18	Dark Green	NA	Shallow silt laden water over mudflats ± emergent vegetation
19	Yellow	4	Undefined: water in river channels
20	Red Brown	4	Disturbed tundra (possible grouping of LCU #14 and #19)
21	Grey	NA	Unknown: disturbed tundra?

NA - *Not Available*

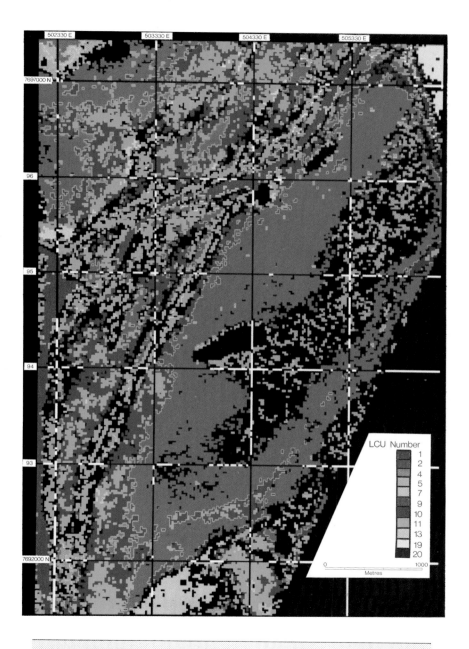

Figure 4. LANDSAT Classification Units (LCUs) of Fish Island, Northwest Territories.

Dickson and Smith

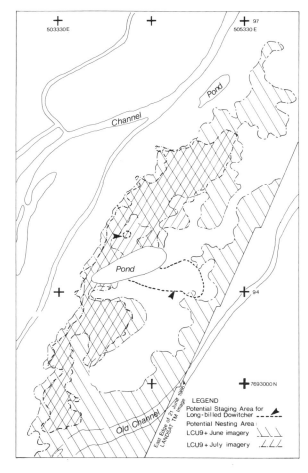

LEGEND

Potential Staging Area for
Long-billed Dowitcher _ _ _ _ _ ◢

Potential Nesting Area:

LCU9 + June imagery \\\\

LCU9 + July imagery ▱▱▱

Figure 5. Potential nesting areas for whimbrel, stilt sandpiper, hudsonian godwit and long-billed dowitcher on Fish Island, Northwest Territories.

times using the June TMI analysis although all were within 60 m of being included. Whimbrel were within the nesting area defined using July TMI 12 of 16 times with 4 nests being within 10 metres and 15 of 16 times using June TMI. We also examined the bird sighting data collected along the grid system.

We used a chi-square test (Conover, 1980) to define whether the distribution of LCUs within 90 m of each grid line were the same in grid segments where shorebirds of a given species were seen as compared with those where no observations were made.

The results of these tests indicate that all priority species along with semipalmated and pectoral sandpipers (*Calidris pusilla* (Linnaeus) and *C. melanotos* (Vieillot)) and red-necked and red phalaropes (*Phalaropus lobatus* (Linnaeus) and *P. fulicaria* (Linnaeus)) significantly differentiate ($p < 0.05$) the habitat (LCUs) which they use. There is however, an overlap in the habitats (LCUs) being used by each species observed on Fish Island. The sample (number of observations on grid segments) were small for red phalaropes and semipalmated sandpipers and moderate for long-billed dowitchers. The lack of data points suggests that semi-palmated sandpipers do not use low-centred polygon habitat for nesting. It also suggests that although long-billed dowitchers do nest in

Dickson and Smith

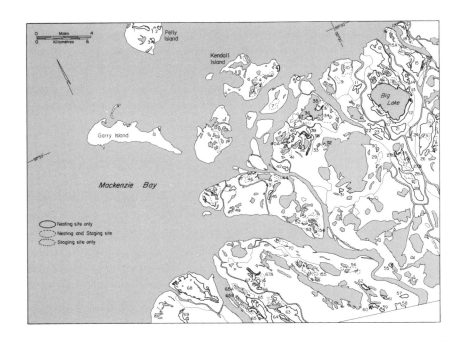

Figure 6. Potential nesting and staging sites defined using LANDSAT TM imagery in the main study area and the Kendell Island subarea, Mackenzie River Delta, Northwest Territories.

low-centred polygon habitat, they may prefer drier areas outside the study area. Information from other biologists suggests that long-billed dowitchers are more common in other areas along the Beaufort Sea including the Tuktoyaktuk Peninsula (D.L. Dickson, pers. comm.) and the Yukon North Slope (D.L. Dickson, pers. comm. and Dickson *et al.*, 1988).

We also observed significant differentiation in the use of habitat when we plotted only those observations which fell within the potential nesting area defined for the priority shorebird species using the June imagery (Figure 5 nesting area: June). When only observations falling within the potential nesting area as defined using the July imagery was used (Figure 5), all species except long-billed dowitchers showed a significant differentiation ($p < 0.05$) of the habitats they use. This suggests that the July imagery alone (assuming that shorebird species were sighted in the preferred nesting areas) is unsuitable for defining potential nest sites of long-billed dowitchers on the Mackenzie River Delta.

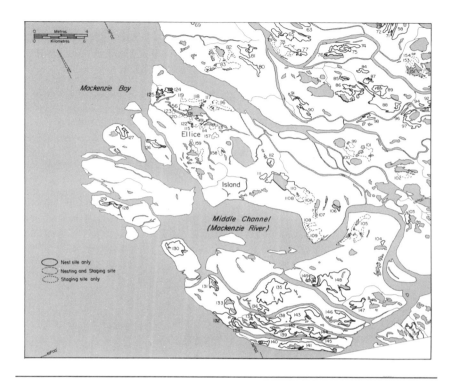

Figure 7. Potential nesting and staging sites defined using LANDSAT TM imagery, Ellice Island Subarea, Mackenzie River Delta, Northwest Territories.

We used a normal approximation to the binomial distribution (Mendenhall, 1979) to test whether the proportions of each LCU type were the same where each species was seen compared to where it was absent. For these tests we pooled the LCU data on all segments where a species was observed and conducted four different tests:

1. including data from all segments surveyed on Fish Island;
2. including data from only those segments falling within the area identified as nesting habitat defined using the June 1986 imagery;
3. including data from only those segments falling within the area identified as nesting habitat defined using July 1986 imagery; and,
4. including data from the area falling only within the overlap nesting area of the June and July imagery interpretation (Figure 5).

Tests were conducted only for LCUs #6 through #12; all other LCUs were represented by less than 100 pixels, scattered throughout the area and were therefore

Dickson and Smith

ignored as inconsequential. The analyses found that whimbrel, hudsonian godwit and pectoral sandpipers and to some extent, stilt sandpipers, are similar in their habitat preference (p < 0.05). All species are selecting for LCU #9. Stilt sandpipers show some difference in their habitat preference in that there is no significant selection or avoidance of LCU #10.

To test whether the results of the LANDSAT analyses, which showed that the percentage of dwarf shrub, graminoid and standing water were the most important habitat variables for the priority shorebird species, we conducted a Three Means Clustering Procedure on the transect data collected throughout the study area (Figure 2; Wilkinson, 1987). LANDSAT analyses identified that the priority shorebird species preferred LCU #9 for nesting. LCU #9 represents a low-centred polygon habitat with greater than 15% graminoid and less than 35% dwarf shrub. The study also indicated that the priority species nested in areas with 15-40% standing water cover.

The Three Means Cluster analysis used all the available transect habitat data. Standing water, graminoid and dwarf shrub were the best discriminating variables, in this order of priority, for defining the three clusters. Thus the assumptions made

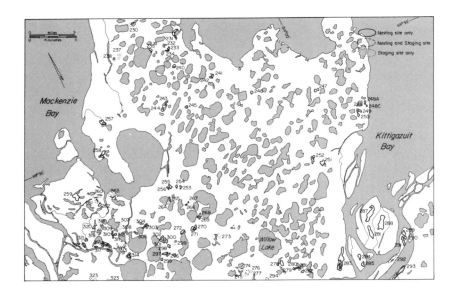

Figure 8. Potential nesting and staging sites defined using LANDSAT TM imagery in the north Richards Island subarea, Northwest Territories.

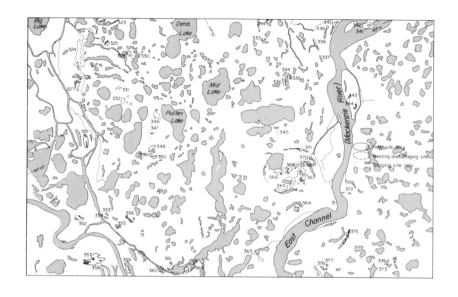

Figure 9. Potential nesting and staging sites defined using LANDSAT TM imagery in the south Richards Island subarea, Northwest Territories.

in preparation for LANDSAT analyses, that these were the three most important variables, was substantiated.

In summary, with the exceptions discussed above, it appears that potential nesting areas defined by LANDSAT TMI analyses are reliable, but that the lack of digital analysis throughout the study area is a shortcoming of the project. Visual interpretation has definite limitations.

DISCUSSION

The collection of 3 years of field data on shorebirds in a small area on Mackenzie River Delta, coupled with LANDSAT Thematic Mapper Imagery enabled the definitions of over 350 potential nesting shorebird sites throughout the Mackenzie River Delta.

LANDSAT MSSI was found to be far inferior to LANDSAT TMI for identification of potential shorebird nesting habitat. The low spatial and spectral resolution and lack of mid-infrared and blue visible bands on MSS imagery severely limits its utility for vegetation and habitat mapping in the level of detail required for this study.

Dickson and Smith

A TMI automated classification produced LCUs representing three shrub dominated vegetation types, three grass/sedge vegetation types, two grass/sedge and water complex types, four water and/or emergent vegetation complex types and two barren LCU types.

This project shows that both visual and computer-aided methods of analysis of LANDSAT TM imagery can be used separately and together for identification of potential nesting shorebird habitat. In addition, moderately detailed vegetation types can be identified both visually and digitally on TM imagery of this low-arctic wetland environment.

The project also demonstrated that the annual spring flood is a major factor in controlling the nesting location of shorebirds. Future research to enable modelling of flood levels on the outer Delta given various ice-jamming and break-up scenarios would provide a means for monitoring or mitigating the effects of future developments affecting the hydrological cycle and levels of the Mackenzie River.

Studies, to evaluate the affects global warming may have on Mackenzie River flows and erosion/deposition of sediments on the outer Delta, are imperative to maintaining and monitoring wildlife using the outer Mackenzie Delta in the future.

ACKNOWLEDGEMENTS

The authors wish to thank the following people and agencies for their assistance in this project. John Ostrick and his staff of the Inuvik Research Laboratory, Inuvik, Northwest Territories, and the Polar Continental Shelf Project for logistic support. Margaret Skeel, Dr. J.P. Meyers and Dr. R.I.G. Morrison for their advice and assistance. We also thank the numerous people who volunteered their time to assist in the field program.

REFERENCES

CONOVER, W.J., 1980. Practical nonparametric statistics. Second Edition, John Wiley and Sons, Toronto, Ontario, 493 pp.

DICKSON, D.L., H.L. DICKSON and G.M. AIUDI, 1988. Bird surveys at Stokes Point and Phillips Bay, Yukon in 1983. Technical Report Series No.40, Canadian Wildlife Service, Western and Northern Region, Environment Canada, Edmonton, Alberta, 117 pp.

JAQUES, D.R., 1987. LANDSAT thematic mapper imagery for analyses of shorebird habitat and vegetation in the outer MacKenzie Delta area, N.W.T. Unpublished report to Canadian Wildlife Service, Environment Canada, Edmonton, Alberta, March 30, 64 pp.

MENDENHALL, W., 1979. Introduction to probability and statistics. 5th Edition, Doxbury Press, North Scituate, Massachusetts, 594 pp.

Van TREES, H.L., 1968. Part 1. Detection, estimation and linear modulation theory. In - Detection, Estimation and Modulation Theory, John Wiley and Sons, New York, 3 volumes

WILKINSON, L., 1987. "SYSTAT": a system for statistics. SYSTAT Inc., Evanston, Illinois

MONITORING WHITE SPRUCE COMMUNITIES ON THE MACKENZIE DELTA WITH SATELLITES

C.M. Pearce

Department of Geography
University of Western Ontario
Social Sciences Centre
London, Ontario
N6A 5C2   CANADA

ABSTRACT

White spruce forests occupy elevated surfaces on the upper Mackenzie Delta. White spruce woodlands have evolved on sites that are not flooded under the modern fluvial regime.   LANDSAT TM data were used to identify spruce-dominated communities on the upper Delta. Differences in albedo between spruce forests and woodlands were recorded by the satellite sensors. It is proposed that changes within white spruce communities can be used as indicators of environmental change on the Mackenzie Delta that can be detected and monitored by orbiting satellites.

INTRODUCTION

One of the most striking features of the Mackenzie Delta is the complex network of channels and lakes and the distinctive arrangement of plant assemblages along flood-related gradients adjacent to these water bodies. Flooding, the annual influx of sediment, and erosion have maintained much of the Delta in the early- to mid-successional stages, but late-successional forests and woodlands dominated by white spruce have developed on the most elevated surfaces (Cordes *et al.*, 1984; Gill, 1971; Mackay, 1963; Pearce *et al.*, 1988).

White spruce (*Picea glauca* [Moench] Voss var. *albertiana*) reaches its most northerly extent in Canada on the Mackenzie Delta. White spruce forests on the Delta are maintained by periodic deposition of alluvium during spring break-up flooding (which provides a mineral seedbed and reduces competition from ground-cover vegetation), and summer temperatures occasionally warm enough for ecesis. However, white spruce woodlands have developed on some sites on the upper delta plain (Pearce *et al.*, 1988). These sites are either so elevated or are so far from active channels that they are no longer flooded, initiating changes in species composition, especially in the ground layers. Successful recruitment of spruce seedlings within these woodlands has not occurred and a ground cover dominated by lichens, crowberry, labrador tea, arctic bearberry, and bilberry plants, also characteristic of tundra vegetation to the west and east of the Delta, has developed.

Changes within vegetation assemblages dominated by white spruce could be used as indicators of environmental change. As white spruce is at its physiological limits of tolerance on the Mackenzie Delta, it is very susceptible to hydrological alteration, changes in climate, and other kinds of environmental disturbance. Spruce-dominated ecosystems have been mapped in a few small areas on the Delta using large-scale aerial photographs combined with ground sampling (Cordes *et al.*, 1984). However, this data base is limited and the storage format does not allow easy retrieval to analyse and monitor vegetation changes.

Forests and woodlands should have different albedo characteristics related to differences in tree cover that either obscures or reveals reflectance from the ground surface. Albedo information from the earth's surface is collected on a regular basis by orbiting satellites, and this information can be purchased for spectral analysis and mapping. Ahern and Archibald (1986), Dey and Richards (1981), Harvie *et al.* (1982), Nelson *et al.* (1984), and Teillet *et al.* (1981) review the utility of satellite data to inventory and monitor northern forests. On the Mackenzie Delta, satellite data have been used to monitor ice break-up (Dey *et al.*, 1977; Dey, 1980), shorebird nesting habitat (Dickson and Smith, 1991), and land- and water-cover types in the outer delta (Tarnocai and Kristof, 1976) and between Inuvik and Aklavik (Vieweg, 1988). The unique characteristics of space imagery, especially the improved geometric and radiometric capabilities of present satellite sensors, could provide the means to identify and monitor white spruce ecosystems on the Delta on a spatial and temporal basis.

Information on species composition and structure and the spatial relationships between white-spruce dominated vegetation and the physical environment, collected from study areas on the upper Mackenzie Delta between 1980 and 1987 (Cordes *et al.*, 1984; Pearce *et al.*, 1988), was compared to LANDSAT TM (thematic mapper) spectral data. The detection of areas characterized by woodlands was of particular interest as these ecosystems indicate a vegetation response to changes in the flooding environment. This paper will demonstrate the utility of satellite data for identifying and monitoring forested surfaces in such a complex and dynamic system as the Mackenzie Delta.

STUDY AREA

The Mackenzie Delta occupies part of the Arctic Coastal Plain between 67 to 70°N and 134 to 136°W within the high subarctic and low arctic climatic zones. The Mackenzie River divides into two large channels -- East Channel flowing to Kugmallit Bay and Middle Channel flowing to Mackenzie Bay -- and numerous small distributaries at Point Separation 20-km below Arctic Red River (Figure 1). The Peel and Rat Rivers enter the Delta to the west of Point Separation and carry water to Shallow Bay via Peel and West Channels. The amount and texture of sediment deposited onto delta surfaces during spring ice break-up flooding varies greatly due to differences in the flood regime in a particular year and to site variability because of topography and vegetation cover: 5 to 15 cm·yr^{-1} of sandy to silty alluvium onto aggrading point bars, 0.05 to 5 cm·yr^{-1} of silty to silty-clay alluvium into lakes, and only a few mm of silty alluvium onto the delta plain if the break-up peak is high enough (Mackay, 1963; Gill, 1971; Cordes *et al.*, 1984; Pearce, 1986). The delta plain is the highest and oldest surface occupying 20 to 40% of the land surface on the upper Delta. Meandering channels and expanding thermokarst lakes are continuously destroying parts of the present delta plain.

The frequency and duration of flooding, the amount and texture of sediment deposited during flooding, and temperatures and precipitation during the growing season are important environmental parameters that act in a complex way to determine plant distribution on the delta (Gill, 1971; Cordes *et al.*, 1984; Pearce, 1986). Sedges, horsetails, and pondweeds dominate channel and lake shorelines. Willow and alder occupy levees throughout the Delta; balsam poplar and white spruce are found on the most elevated sites in the upper Delta. In the lower Delta, trees are absent and willow and alder occupy the highest sites above extensive sedge-cottongrass tussock meadows.

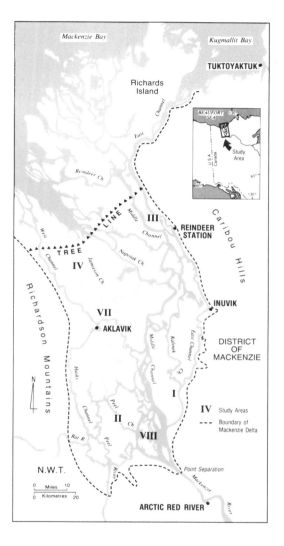

Figure 1. The Mackenzie Delta study areas.

METHODS AND MATERIALS

Vegetation and Environmental Measurements

Ground measurements on the vegetation and physical environment were collected between 1980 and 1983 from six study areas on the upper Delta (Figure 1): Areas 1 (near East Channel), II (Peel Channel), and VIII (alluvial islands of Middle Channel) representing the "inner" Delta, and Areas III (East Channel), IV (Jamieson Channel), and VII (Taylor Channel) the "middle" Delta (Cordes *et al.*, 1984; Pearce, 1986). Each study area enclosed an area 10 km x 10 km. Data on species composition; percent canopy cover, density, and height of each species; and ages of trees and shrubs were used to classify the vegetation into plant communities. The vegetation data and measurements within each plant community on elevation above and distance from channels or lakes, frequency and duration of flooding, sediment deposition during flooding, soil type, drainage, and maximum depth to permafrost during the growing season were used to characterize delta ecosystems based on relationships between the vegetation and the fluvial regime (Cordes *et al.*, 1984). These ecosystems were mapped within each study area using natural colour aerial photographs flown in August 1980 by B.C. Hydro, Vancouver, B.C. Aerial observations during flights between the study areas and additional ground measurements were collected by the author in 1986 and 1987 to more precisely describe the distribution and character of the white spruce-dominated ecosystems on the upper delta (Pearce *et al.*, 1988).

Satellite Measurements

Digital data for a cloud-free LANDSAT Thematic Mapper overpass on August 7, 1985 over the Mackenzie Delta (scene ID: 50524-195818 centred at 68°27'N) were purchased from the Prince Albert satellite station for analysis on a 386 computer located in the Department of Geography, The University of Western Ontario, using PCI EASI/PACE image-analysis software. The quantized digital values for pixels with 30 m x 30 m ground resolution were examined for data redundancy. Radiance data for TM wavelengths 2 (green), 3 (red), and 4 (near-infrared) were selected for further analysis.

The radiance data were enhanced to improve them for visual analysis and interpretation. Because the satellite sensors record upwelling radiance from both poorly-illuminated and well-illuminated surfaces, only a small proportion of the total measurement scale is used for any particular scene resulting in a low-contrast image when the data are displayed on a video display monitor. Histograms for the radiance data were displayed for each wavelength. Minimum and maximum radiance values for each wavelength were "stretched" between 0 (no reflectance) and 255 (very high reflectance) using a histogram equalization procedure that weights radiance values based on their frequency of occurrence (Curran, 1985). The enhanced data for each wavelength were displayed separately and in combination for each of the six study areas and compared to baseline maps and aerial photographs.

The raw radiance values for each wavelength were analyzed to identify unique spectral signatures associated with the dominant cover types described for the upper Mackenzie Delta by Cordes *et al.* (1984), Gill (1971), and Pearce (1986). Sixty pixels were measured for each cover type in each study area and the radiance values associated with these pixels were summarized into means and standard deviations. The spectral information for the white spruce ecosystems was extracted and used to detect spruce forests and woodlands throughout the upper Delta. The spectral information was printed from the display to hardcopy using a Tektronix 4696 colour inkjet printer and compared to topographic maps and photomosaics to identify exactly the location of the spruce woodlands on the Mackenzie Delta.

RESULTS AND DISCUSSION

Characteristics of White Spruce Ecosystems on the Mackenzie Delta

Eighteen alluvial ecosystems dominated by aquatic macrophytes, sedge, horsetail, willow, alder, balsam poplar, and spruce have been described for the upper Mackenzie Delta (Cordes and McLennan, 1991; Cordes *et al.*, 1984; Gill, 1971; Pearce, 1986). Of these, four ecosystems dominated by white spruce were distinguished based on differences in species composition in the ground vegetation, tree density and age, and site characteristics. Complete descriptions are given in Cordes *et al.* (1984) and Pearce *et al.* (1988) and will only be summarized here.

White spruce/alder-bearberry ecosystems occupy elevated sites on point bars, channels levees, and lakeshores, and lower elevations on the delta plain throughout the upper Delta (elevation range 7 to 8 m above autumn low water near Point Separation and 3 to 4 m between Aklavik, Inuvik, and treeline). Frozen soils were measured 50 to 70 cm below the surface in mid-August. This forest type is characterized by a diverse and relatively luxuriant cover of shrubs and herbs. White spruce trees (to 250-years old with a mean canopy cover of 25% and density of 15 trees within sampling plots 10 m x 10 m) are maintained by flooding every 5 to 10 years. Mean annual sedimentation rates of 2 mm to 2 cm were measured within these forests between 1980 and 1987.

White spruce/feathermoss forests occupy elevated sites on the delta plain that are flooded during only the highest spring ice break-up events every 10 to 50 years (elevation ranges 8 to 9 m above ALW near Point Separation and 4 to 5 m between Aklavik, Inuvik, and treeline). Permafrost is reached at 20 to 60 cm below the surface. This forest is distinguished by organic acidic soils, a dense cover of white spruce (mean canopy cover 45% and density 20 trees in sample plots) to 400-years old, and a poorly-developed ground cover dominated by feathermoss. Only a few of the white spruce/feathermoss forests were flooded during the record peaks in 1982, and seedlings were measured only on sites that received some alluvium during previous flood events in 1961 and 1972.

White spruce/feathermoss forests on the Mackenzie Delta appear to be developing into white spruce/heath-lichen woodlands on the most elevated and relatively xeric sites (elevation range 9 to 10 m above ALW near Point Separation and 5 to 6 m between Aklavik, Inuvik, and treeline) (Figure 2). Reconnaissance by the author in 1986 and 1987 indicated that these woodlands appeared to be restricted to those areas on the upper Delta drained by the Peel River and its distributaries (Figure 5), but many parts of the Delta could not be checked due to time and budget constraints. White spruce are very old (200 to 450 years) and sparse (only 10% mean cover and density of 5 trees in sample plots), and no spruce seedlings were measured in these woodlands between 1980 and 1987. Thick organic substrates, permafrost depths of 30 to 50 cm, and a luxuriant ground cover of lichens, crowberry, blueberry and other heaths with tundra affinities indicate that these sites have not been flooded for a very long time. Past flooding regimes and the formation of ice lenses within the substrate have elevated these woodlands well above the modern flooding and erosional regime in some parts of the Delta (Gill, 1973; Mackay, 1963; Pearce *et al.*, 1988).

Figure 2. White spruce woodlands on an elevated site (5.5-m above ALW) north of Aklavik. The dotted line marks flood height in 1982, a year of very high break-up peaks on the Delta. Note the sparse spruce cover and the lichen understory. (Photograph: D. McLennan)

White spruce-tamarack/sphagnum moss woodlands are evolving on poorly-drained sites between elevated, fluvially-inactive, point-bar levees between Point Separation and Aklavik. Permafrost within 20 to 40 cm of the surface impedes drainage and the elevated levees block floodwaters during spring ice break-up. Plant succession is initiated by sedges and cottongrass eventually developing into a woodland more characteristic of bogs on the Peel Plateau to the south of the Mackenzie Delta. White spruce and tamarack are stunted (3-m tall), sparse (canopy cover 5 to 10% and density 5 trees in sample plots), and old (to 350 years), but are maintained by a few seedlings colonizing elevated frost hummocks within the sphagnum.

Table 1. Mean radiance measurements, Mackenzie Delta cover types LANDSAT TM, August 7, 1985.

COVER TYPE	NATURAL COLOUR	COLOUR ON FCIR IMAGE (ON DISPLAY MONITOR)	MEAN RADIANCE*		
			GREEN	RED	IR
Spruce/alder-bearberry (tree cover 25%; shrub/herb cover 60%; lichen/moss cover 10%)	Medium Green	Orange-red to Red	24.4 (1.7)**	19.6 (1.9)	67.5 (3.5)
Spruce/feathermoss (tree cover 45%; shrub/herb cover 15%; moss cover 45%)	Dark Green	Dark Red	20.7 (1.3)	15.6 (1.2)	45.2 (8.7)
Spruce woodland (tree cover 5 to 10%; shrub cover 5%; heath/lichen/sphagnum cover 50%)	Green-Brown to Rust	Cyan	23.7 (1.8)	24.5 (1.9)	51.8 (6.6)
Alder-willow	Bright Green	Orange-pink	28.6	19.4	78.2
Mature willow (sparse)	Dull Green	Mauve	23.4	20.5	43.2
Pioneer willow	Light Green	Pink	24.7	18.4	60.5
Clear water	Deep Blue	Black	15.8	15.0	9.5
Silty water	Light Green to Light Blue	Blue	30.2	30.0	14.5

Raw (i.e. not enhanced) values, based on a possible scale of 0 (no reflectance) to 255 (highest reflectance).
**Standard deviations (shown only for spruce communities).*

Characteristics of Spectral Patterns Associated with White Spruce Ecosystems

Figures 3 and 4 show the false-colour composite images produced from the enhanced radiance data for Area II (on Peel Channel in the west inner Delta) and Area III (on East Channel in the east middle Delta). On these images, the radiance values for green vegetation are depicted as orange-red (white spruce with an alder-bearberry understory), dark red (dense white spruce with a feathermoss understory), mauve (mature willow), pink (pioneer willow), and orange-pink (alder); and for water as black (clear water) or light to medium blue (turbid water) (Table 1).

Extensive areas of cyan appear on the Area II image adjacent to meander bends on "Bow-Smashed-In Channel" (local name from Cordes *et al.*, 1984) and abandoned channel segments north of Peel Channel. These areas correlate exactly with areas of white spruce woodland mapped in detail between 1980 and 1983 and observed during aerial reconnaissance in 1986 and 1987. This spectral signature does not appear on the image for Area III, nor have naturally-occurring woodlands been identified and mapped in this area.

Pearce

Table 1 shows the mean raw radiance values for the visible and near-infrared wavelengths as measured from each cover type in all of the study areas on the upper Delta. Dense deciduous vegetation on the Delta, represented by the pioneer willow and alder-willow cover types, exhibits low radiance values in the green and red wavelengths but comparatively high values in the near-infrared wavelength. High radiances values in the near-infrared wavelength are also shown for the white spruce/alder-bearberry forest. In contrast, closed-canopy spruce/feathermoss forests and open spruce/heath-lichen or spruce-tamarack/sphagnum woodlands exhibit lower reflectance in the near-infrared wavelength and subtle differences in the red wavelength. Although the differences between the radiance values associated with the spruce woodlands and the spruce forests were subtle, they were distinctive enough to label the three spruce cover types. Radiance values in the green and near-infrared wavelengths separated the spruce/feathermoss and spruce/alder-bearberry cover types respectively (significant at 95%, Scheffe F-test), while all cover types were separated in the red wavelength (significant at 95%).

The spectral patterns described above require explanation. Radiance data collected by satellite sensors for each wavelength are loaded to one of three colour guns on an RGB video display monitor. In this research, TM2 (green) was displayed as blue, TM3 (red) as green, and TM4 (near infrared) as red to produce a standard false-colour infrared (FCIR) image on the monitor and on hardcopy. In actively-photosynthesizing plants, molecular absorption by chlorophylls within plant cells contributes to low reflection of radiant energy in the visible wavelengths; but multiple scattering within the spongy mesophyll gives high reflection in the near infrared, and vigorous green vegetation appears red on FCIR images. These spectral patterns can vary depending on plant density and canopy cover, leaf colour, the proportion of green and brown biomass, the geometric arrangement of leaves and stems, and the amount of shadow cast by standing plants, parameters that in combination can amplify or dampen spectral response.

On the Mackenzie Delta, conifers such as white spruce and deciduous shrubs such as willow and alder have different spectral properties because of differences in surface leaf colour and internal structure that affect reflectance in the visible and infrared wavelengths. The more-open white spruce/alder-bearberry communities are spectrally distinct from the darker-coloured, closed-canopy spruce/feathermoss communities because of differences in tree cover which either reveals or obscures the understory. In other words, the satellite sensors record what is "seen" from an aerial viewpoint. In the spruce/feathermoss cover type, what is "seen" is a dark green canopy of needles and black shadows between the upright trees, and on a FCIR image this type appears dark red; in the spruce/alder-bearberry cover type, what is "seen" is the vigorous deciduous understory, and on a FCIR image this type appears bright red.

The spruce woodlands are characterized by widely-spaced trees that also expose the understory. However, the lichens that dominate this understory have reflectance properties different from green vegetation (Gauslaa, 1984; Petzold and Goward, 1988). Where lichen cover is high on the Delta, the ground surface appears a

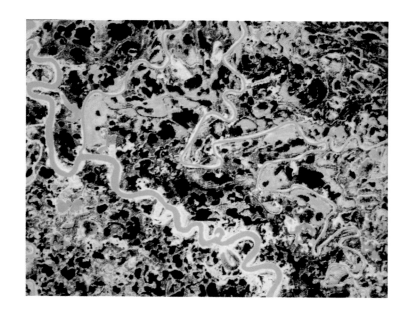

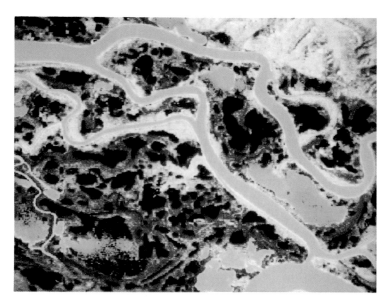

Figures 3 and 4. LANDSAT TM images of Area II on Peel Channel (top) and Area III on East Channel (bottom) (scale 1:73,626).

yellow-white from above rather than green. The low-growing heath species (arctic bearberry, crowberry, and bilberry), feathermosses, and sphagnum mosses, also characteristic of the woodland understory, appear a green-brown to rust colour from above. Reflectance from the heath-lichen-moss ground cover was higher (significant at 95%) in the red wavelength than the other spruce communities (Table 1), a spectral response similar to that from non-vegetated surfaces resulting in a blue-green colour on a FCIR composite (Figure 3).

Differences in turbidity were detectable in all wavelengths, although this analysis was not part of the research. Generally, absorption of radiant energy by water increases with increasing wavelength. However, the degree of absorption is proportional to the depth, concentration, texture, and colour of suspended and dissolved mineral and organic material. Thus, radiant energy is almost completely absorbed by clear water, especially in the infrared. In addition, spectral information from the ground surface in the blue wavelengths is blocked. Thus, even though clear water on the Delta is dark blue, these water bodies appear black on FCIR images. Large quantities of alluvium suspended throughout the water column will reflect some of the radiant energy in both the visible and infrared wavelengths back to the sensor. On the other hand, light to moderate quantities of alluvium suspended in the water column below the surface or visible from the bottom of clear shallow water bodies may impart a colour difference in the visible wavelengths but will not contribute to reflectance from the water surface in the near-infrared wavelength. Turbid water, then, will appear as various shades of blue on FCIR images, depending on the sediment load.

Extrapolating the Radiance Data

The relationships established between the radiance measurements and specific cover types within the study areas were extrapolated to satellite data for the entire upper Mackenzie Delta (an area approximately 75 km x 50 km) and printed as a colour mosaic. Examination of the hardcopy and comparison with topographic maps and photo-mosaics indicated that, although the spruce forest cover types are found throughout the upper Delta, the woodland cover type is generally restricted to the west Delta between the Richardson Mountains and Middle Channel from the Peel River almost to treeline (Figure 5). More specifically, the woodlands are most common on what appear to be fluvially-inactive sites between Husky and Phillips Channels, Phillips and Peel Channels, and Peel and Middle Channels in the inner Delta; and in the middle Delta within an area bounded by Esau, Enoch, and Pokiak Channels southeast of Aklavik and another area bounded by Jamieson, Schooner, and Aklavik Channels northeast of Aklavik (Figure 5).

CONCLUSIONS

Forests dominated by white spruce characterize elevated sites on the Mackenzie Delta that periodically receive small amounts of alluvium during spring ice break-up flooding. The present lack of flooding on the most elevated or distant sites is a major factor responsible for the evolution of white spruce woodlands in those parts of the Delta drained by the Peel River and its distributaries. This suggests that some sites in these areas are becoming fluvially-inactive compared to areas east of Middle Channel. In an area already marginal for seed production and ecesis, these woodlands could well develop into plant assemblages more typical of the tundra with the death of the few remaining trees and lack of restocking, provided that the present fluvial and climatic regimes within the Delta continue.

This paper has demonstrated that white spruce forests and woodlands on the Delta exhibit differences in albedo that can be detected by satellite sensors. It is proposed that changes within white spruce ecosystems can be used as indicators of environmental change on the upper Mackenzie Delta and that these changes can be monitored by orbiting satellites.

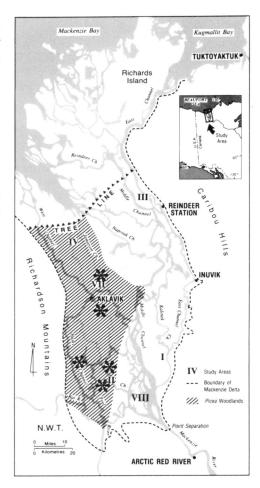

Figure 5. The distribution of white spruce woodlands on the Mackenzie Delta, especially at locations indicated by an asterisk (*).

ACKNOWLEDGEMENTS

I would like to thank the following agencies and individuals who contributed in a major way to this research: the Scientific Resources Centre, Inuvik, N.W.T. and Polar Continental Shelf Project, Tuktoyaktuk, N.W.T. for accommodation and logistic support; B.C. Hydro, Vancouver, B.C., Water Survey of Canada, Inuvik, N.W.T., and the National Hydrology Research Institute, Saskatoon, Saskatchewan for hydrological data; Cordes and Associates, Rolling Hills, Alberta for data collected between 1980 and

1983; the Science Institute of the Northwest Territories for permission to conduct the research; Donna Limpert and Lori Waldbrook for assistance in the field in 1986 and 1987 respectively; Department of Geography, The University of Western Ontario, London, Ontario for cartography; Ian Craig, Department of Biology, The University of Western Ontario, for photography. The remote sensing research was funded through grants to C.M. Pearce from NSERC (through The University of Western Ontario) and Dean's Grants (through the Faculty of Social Sciences, UWO).

REFERENCES

AHERN, F.J. and P.D. ARCHIBALD, 1986. Thematic mapper information about Canadian forests: early results from across the country. Proceedings, 10th Canadian Symposium on Remote Sensing, 5-8 May 1986, Edmonton, Alberta, Vol.II, 683-697

CORDES, L.D. and D.S. MCLENNAN, 1991. Ecology of aquatic-macrophyte communities in Mackenzie Delta lakes. In - Mackenzie Delta: Environmental Interactions and Implications of Development, P. Marsh and C.S.L. Ommanney (Editors), Proceedings of the Workshop on the Mackenzie Delta, 17-18 October 1989, Saskatoon, Saskatchewan, NHRI Symposium No.4, National Hydrology Research Institute, Environment Canada, Saskatoon, Saskatchewan, 121-122

CORDES, L.D., D. MCLENNAN and C.M. PEARCE, 1984. Alluvial ecosystems in the Mackenzie Delta, N.W.T. Research Contract, L.D. Cordes & Associates for B.C. Hydro, Vancouver, B.C., 2 volumes

CURRAN, P.J., 1985. Principles of remote sensing. Longman, New York, N.Y., 282 pp.

DEY, B., 1980. Orbital sensing of Mackenzie Bay ice dynamics. Arctic, 33(2), 280-291

DEY, B., H. MOORE and A.F. GREGORY, 1977. The use of satellite imagery for monitoring ice break-up along the Mackenzie River, N.W.T. Arctic, 30(4), 234-242

DEY, B. and J.H. RICHARDS 1981. The Canadian North: utility of remote sensing for environmental monitoring. Remote Sensing of Environment, 11(1), 57-72

DICKSON, H.L. and A.R. SMITH, 1991. Use of LANDSAT thematic mapper and multi-spectral scanning imagery to identify habitats and shorebird nesting areas on the outer Mackenzie River Delta, N.W.T. In - Mackenzie Delta: Environmental Interactions and Implications of Development, P. Marsh and C.S.L. Ommanney (Editors), Proceedings of the Workshop on the Mackenzie Delta, 17-18 October 1989, Saskatoon, Saskatchewan, NHRI Symposium No.4, National Hydrology Research Institute, Environment Canada, Saskatoon, Saskatchewan, 91-106

GAUSLAA, Y., 1984. Infrared and visible reflectance in different lichen species and its ecological significance. Holarctic Ecology, 7(1), 13-22

GILL, D., 1971. Vegetation and environment in the Mackenzie River Delta, N.W.T.: a study in subarctic ecology. Ph.D. thesis, Department of Geography, University of British Columbia, Vancouver, British Columbia, 694 pp.

Pearce

GILL, D., 1973. Ecological modifications caused by the removal of tree and shrub canopies in the Mackenzie Delta. Arctic, 26(2), 95-111

HARVIE, J.M., J. CIHLAR and C. GOODFELLOW, 1982. Surface cover mapping in the arctic through satellite remote sensing. Users' Manual 82-1, Canada Centre for Remote Sensing, Energy, Mines and Resources Canada, Ottawa, Ontario, 61 pp.

MACKAY, J.R., 1963. The Mackenzie Delta area, N.W.T. Geographical Branch Memoir No.8, Department of Mines and Technical Surveys, Ottawa, Ontario, 202 pp.

NELSON, R.F., R.S. LATTY and G. MOTT, 1984. Classifying northern forests using thematic mapper simulator data. Photogrammetric Engineering and Remote Sensing, 50(5), 607-617

PEARCE, C.M., 1986. The distribution and ecology of the shoreline vegetation on the Mackenzie Delta, N.W.T. Ph.D. thesis, Department of Geography, University of Calgary, Calgary, Alberta, 400 pp.

PEARCE, C.M., D. MCLENNAN and L.D. CORDES, 1988. The evolution and maintenance of white spruce woodlands on the Mackenzie Delta, N.W.T., Canada. Holarctic Ecology, 11(4), 248-258

PETZOLD, D.E. and S.N. GOWARD, 1988. Reflectance spectra of subarctic lichens. Remote Sensing of Environment, 24(3), 481-492

TARNOCAI, C. and S.J. KRISTOF, 1976. Computer-aided classification of land and water bodies using LANDSAT data, Mackenzie Delta area, N.W.T., Canada. Arctic and Alpine Research, 8(2), 151-159

TEILLET, P.M., B. GUINDON and D.G. GOODENOUGH, 1981. Forest classification using simulated LANDSAT-D thematic mapper data. Canadian Journal of Remote Sensing, 7(1), 51-60

VIEWEG, M., 1988. Fort McPherson/Mackenzie Delta forest inventory. Remote Sensing in the Northwest Territories, 1(2), 2

ECOLOGY OF AQUATIC-MACROPHYTE COMMUNITIES IN MACKENZIE DELTA LAKES

L.D. Cordes[1] and D.S. McLennan[2]

[1]Department of Geography
University of Calgary
Calgary, Alberta
T2N 1N4   CANADA

[2]Faculty of Forestry
University of British Columbia
Vancouver, British Columbia
V6T 1W5   CANADA

ABSTRACT

Mackenzie Delta lakes are characterized by a luxuriant growth of submerged macrophytic vegetation which supports large populations of muskrat, fish and waterfowl. It is postulated that hydro-electric development in the Mackenzie drainage basin will alter flooding effects in Mackenzie Delta lakes and that this will in turn alter ecological factors controlling macrophyte communities. The study was undertaken to examine the relationship between the distribution of aquatic-macrophyte communities and lake-flooding characteristics in Mackenzie Delta lakes.

Lakes were chosen for sampling according to a lake-classification system developed in Cordes and McLennan (1984). This system classifies lake types according to flooding characteristics and thus provides a convenient method for stratification of sampling effort. Thirty-two lakes were sampled using a point-sampling method with point samples ranging from 32 in a small, unconnected lake to 457 in a large, connected basin. This sampling method provided frequency data for comparing abundances of macrophyte species in the different lake types. Several multivariate analysis (PCA, DA, CLUSTER) methods were applied to the data and four associations established - 1) P. richardsonii; *2)* Chara; *3)* Eleocharis; *and, 4)* Ceratophyllum. *Maps of the vegetation associations were developed for all lakes sampled using the transect data.*

An analysis of physical limnological data from the lakes identified turbidity and the consequent attenuation of light with depth as the main factor controlling macrophyte distributions in Mackenzie Delta lakes. Differences in flooding effects in the various lake types created variations in lake turbidity with resulting effects on macrophyte distributions and abundances. Thus the productivity of macrophytes in Mackenzie Delta lakes will vary according to how much of the basin falls within the critical depth range as determined by the light environment in that lake. Any changes in flooding behaviour that alter light environments in Mackenzie Delta lakes will alter macrophyte productivity according to this relationship between abundance, basin morphometry and lake turbidity.

REFERENCES

CORDES, L.D. AND D.S. McLENNAN, 1984. The estimation of sedimentation rates using ^{137}Cs in lakes of the Mackenzie Delta. Unpublished report, L. Cordes and Associates, Calgary, Alberta for British Columbia Power and Authority, Vancouver, British Columbia, August 27, 68 pp.

STABLE ISOTOPES OF SULPHUR AND CARBON AS TRACERS OF FEEDING LOCATIONS AMONG BROAD WHITEFISH POPULATIONS IN THE LOWER MACKENZIE RIVER BASIN: PRELIMINARY RESULTS

R.H. Hesslein, M.J. Capel, D.E. Fox[1], and K.A. Hallard[2]

Department of Fisheries and Oceans
Freshwater Institute
501 University Crescent
Winnipeg, Manitoba
R3T 2N6   CANADA

[1]Present address:
Department of Chemistry
University of Calgary
Calgary, Alberta
T2N 1N4   CANADA

[2]Present address:
Water Quality Division
Saskatchewan Environment and Public Safety
3085 Albert Street
Regina, Saskatchewan
S4S 0B1   CANADA

ABSTRACT

Preliminary investigations into the use of the stable isotopes of sulphur and carbon as tracers of fish-feeding locations and migration are reported for broad whitefish of the lower Mackenzie River basin. The isotopic data are interpreted in light of the life history of the species. Analyses of muscle samples from broad whitefish caught in several locations showed ranges of $\delta^{34}S$ of -20 to +5‰ and $\delta^{13}C$ of -35 to -20‰. Ranges reported for fish known to be feeding solely in some of the same locations where the broad whitefish were caught, such as Travaillant Lake and the Kukjuktuk Creek system, were less than 4‰ for both isotopes. The isotopic "fingerprints" of these locations could be identified as loci on a plot of the carbon versus sulphur isotopic values. Many of the broad whitefish were positioned in the loci at which they were caught, but many were also very different in isotopic composition. Some of the broad whitefish had isotopic compositions which were far from any of the loci which could be identified. The study shows clearly that the broad whitefish caught together in spawning aggregation feed consistently in very different locations. The method is very promising for the future interpretation of complex stocks in areas like the lower Mackenzie region. More compositional loci need to be identified and a better understanding of the turnover rates of elements in fish is required to make full use of the data.

INTRODUCTION

Stable isotopes of sulphur, carbon, and nitrogen have been shown to provide excellent insight into food-web structure in lakes in the lower Mackenzie River region, N.W.T., Canada (Hesslein *et al.*, 1991). Sulphur was used in the above study to indicate whether or not fish belonged to the local food web (had the local sulphur isotope signal) or were migrants which had accumulated much of the sulphur in their muscle in other locations. Carbon isotopes, while less interpretable in that study, have been used in many studies as indicators of carbon sources for food webs (Peterson and Fry, 1987; Schell, 1983; Bunn *et al.*, 1989). The basis for use of both of these isotope pairs (34/32 for sulphur and 13/12 for carbon) as indicators of food sources depends on the unaltered assimilation, with respect to isotope ratios, of the sulphur and carbon in food. Small fractionations of carbon isotopes in each step of the food chain (approx. 0.5‰) have been reported (DeNiro and Epstein, 1978). To our knowledge no isotopic fractionation in food chains has been reported for sulphur. The lack of fractionation of sulphur with trophic transfer may be because sulphur-containing amino acids are essential requirements of animals, that is, they do not synthesize those amino acids. Thus, sulphur bonds are not broken and reformed, leaving no opportunity for fractionation.

In this study we have used the stable isotopes of sulphur and carbon to examine the feeding and migration of one species, broad whitefish (*Coregonus nasus*) in the waters of and connected to the lower Mackenzie River. Since we have used mostly large fish of a single species, differences in fractionation of carbon isotopes due to food-web position is likely not important to our interpretation. This cannot be entirely discounted, however, as broad whitefish do have varied diets (Hatfield *et al.*, 1972a). The isotopic composition of sulphur and carbon assigned to food webs of certain known feeding locations was determined in more detailed food-web studies (Hesslein *et al.* 1989, 1991).

Broad whitefish are found throughout the Mackenzie River watershed, as far south as Fort Simpson, N.W.T. (Hatfield *et al.*, 1972a, 1972b). They are occasionally found in brackish waters of the estuary, but generally remain in the nearshore areas (Percy, 1975). The broad whitefish is an important species in the domestic fishery in the Mackenzie Valley (Hatfield *et al.*, 1972a, 1972b). The length-frequency distribution of fish caught near the town of Arctic Red River in 1971 had a mode at 510 mm. This length translates to a weight of about 2.0 kg and would be about 10-years (Hatfield *et al.*, 1972a, 1972b). Reist and Bond (1988) have summarized the life histories of coregonids in the lower Mackenzie River. Immature fish (less than 6 to 8 years) move seasonally between overwintering areas and summer feeding areas. Large numbers of juveniles migrate into the numerous tributary streams along the coast of the Beaufort Sea and on islands. Bond and Erickson (1985) observed hundreds of thousands in the Freshwater Creek system on the Tuktoyaktuk Peninsula in age-stratified migrations in early summer. Overwintering sites are believed to be in the delta channels and estuary. Mature fish also make what are believed to be feeding migrations to the same tributary and coastal streams, but the spawners congregate in the major Delta channels in mid-August through

September before beginning rapid migrations to spawning sites upstream. Spawning is believed to occur in the Mackenzie River at Point Separation near the town of Arctic Red River, and Rampart Rapids (Chang-Kue and Jessop, 1983) as well as in the Peel River, Arctic Red River, and tributary lake systems such as Travaillant Lake (Reist and Bond, 1988; Stein *et al.*, 1973).

METHODS

Carbon and sulphur isotopes were analyzed on portions of the dorsal muscle as described in detail by Hesslein *et al.* (1989). Briefly, carbon dioxide was produced by modified Dumas combustion and cryogenically separated for mass spectrometry. For sulphur isotope analyses wet flesh was digested in concentrated nitric acid, dried and heated to 380°C. The sample was then dissolved in dilute acid and $BaSO_4$ precipitated. This was then thermally decomposed to SO_2. Standard deviation of $\delta^{13}C$ was 0.1‰ and 0.4‰ for $\delta^{34}S$. All values are standardized to PDB for $\delta^{13}C = 0$ and Canyon Diabolo meteorite for $\delta^{34}S = 0$.

Fish were caught by standard netting techniques described by Reist (1987). All fish were taken from the collections of Reist (1987) and all basic information on the fish, i.e., length, weight, sex, maturity, etc. is from that report. That report also provides details of the sampling locations.

RESULTS

Sulphur isotopes in broad whitefish in the Mackenzie River Basin and in coastal drainages to the Beaufort Sea have a large range of values; -20 to +5‰ (Figure 1). In populations which can be identified as local, as in Travaillant Lake (all species but broad whitefish) and the Kukjuktuk Creek system (northern pike), ranges were less than 3‰ (Hesslein *et al.*, 1991). In populations congregated in spawning runs such as the location of Horseshoe Bend and Ramparts Rapids, the range was widest. However, a wide range of values was also present in fish from Campbell Lake and other sites. Broad whitefish caught in Travaillant Lake had the narrowest range of values. Broad whitefish from two Mackenzie Delta lakes, Skidoo and South, also had, with one exception, a narrow range (the number of fish analysed in these systems was however relatively small). All fish from locations with wide ranges covered more-or-less the same range of -15 to +2‰.

The total range of $\delta^{13}C$ values in broad whitefish from all locations was also quite wide; from -20 to -35‰ (Figure 2). However, unlike for sulphur, no collections from a single site cover the entire range. The widest ranges are from the same locations as for sulphur distributions, but are only about 60% of the total $\delta^{13}C$ range. As was describe for the sulphur isotopes, Travaillant Lake and the two delta lakes, Skidoo and South have the narrowest ranges.

Hesslein et al.

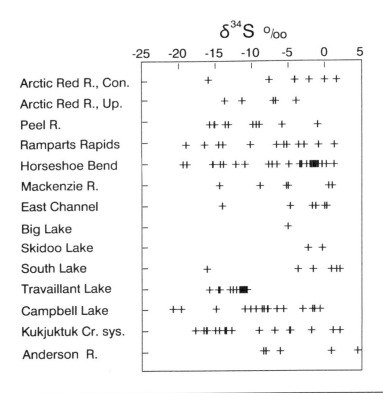

Figure 1. $\delta^{34}S$ in muscle from individual broad whitefish caught at various locations in the lower Mackenzie River region. Abbreviations: Con. = confluence, Up. = upstream and sys. = system.

The two component diagram (Figure 3) describing individual fish in terms of both sulphur- and carbon-isotope composition makes it possible to discriminate between groups of fish. The confidence in this discrimination is enhanced if the $\delta^{34}S$ and $\delta^{13}C$ values characterizing the local food sources are known. Based on the data of Hesslein *et al.* (1989, 1991) we have estimated the range of $\delta^{34}S$ and $\delta^{13}C$ values which would be expected from four sites: the Kukjuktuk Creek system on the Tuktoyaktuk Peninsula, the coastal waters of the Peninsula, the delta lakes near Inuvik (Fee *et al.*, 1988), and Travaillant Lake, a 115 km^2 lake on a tributary of the lower Mackenzie River. Many fish fall in the sulphur-carbon compositional loci of the local populations of the Kukjuktuk Creek system and delta lakes. No fish fall in the locus of local fish in Travaillant although the broad whitefish from Travaillant Lake are near that locus. There does not seem to be a significant influence of

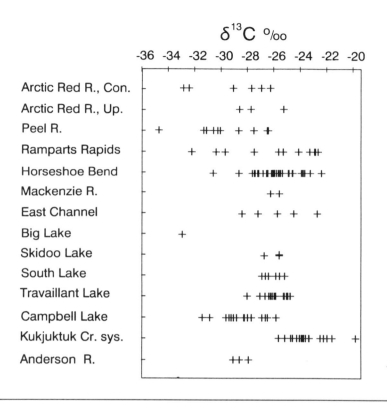

Figure 2. $\delta^{13}C$ in muscle from individual broad whitefish caught at various locations in the lower Mackenzie River region. Abbreviations: Con. = confluence, Up. = upstream and sys. = system.

coastal feeding in the broad whitefish as was noted for lake whitefish from the Kukjuktuk Creek system (Hesslein *et al.,* 1991). Although many fish caught in the Kukjuktuk Creek system and in the Mackenzie River fall within those loci respectively, there are also many fish outside these loci, and even some caught in one location but falling in the other compositional locus.

If the Kukjuktuk Creek system and the delta lakes were the only important feeding areas, we would expect all fish to be linear mixes of the two loci on the $\delta^{34}S$ vs. $\delta^{13}C$ diagram (Figure 3). This is not the case for at least half of the fish analysed. There is very probably at least one other as yet unidentified local loci with the characteristic of very negative $\delta^{13}C$ values. The area of the Peel River is

Hesslein et al.

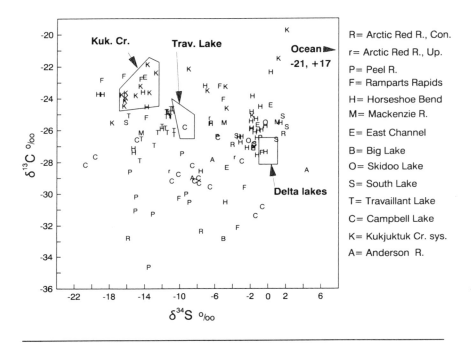

Figure 3. $\delta^{13}C$ and $\delta^{34}S$ in muscle from individual broad whitefish caught at various locations in the lower Mackenzie River region. Polygons outline loci identified for local isotopic composition for some locations.

an interesting candidate because many of the fish caught at that site appear to be influenced by a locus with a composition of $\delta^{34}S$ of about -15‰ and $\delta^{13}C$ of about -34‰.

DISCUSSION

The results of this study demonstrate that there are stocks from different feeding locations in the broad whitefish population. There is evidence that Mackenzie River broad whitefish are structured in distinct genetic stocks (J. Reist, Fisheries and Oceans, Winnipeg, personal communication). It is important to the management of the broad whitefish fishery that the integrity of the stocks is understood and taken into account. Based on the data in Figures 1 and 2, we contend that the broad whitefish caught in spawning runs represent collections of fish which have been feeding in a variety of habitats and have acquired different sulphur isotope values. Considering the wide range of values found at several sites, the broad whitefish in the connected waters of the lower Mackenzie River probably feed in a variety of locations and perhaps half of them feed in a mixture of locations. Because we have analysed primarily mature fish we cannot determine whether this is true of all stages of the life history.

Although we believe that the use of the stable isotopes of sulphur and carbon has provided much additional insight into broad whitefish feeding and migration, there is much more that needs to be known about the isotopes in the various potential feeding sites in the lower Mackenzie River region and about the physiological histories of the elements in fish. Measurements of $\delta^{34}S$ in SO_4 and $\delta^{13}C$ in dissolved inorganic carbon in the waters of the Mackenzie River basin suggest that there are significant differences in the signals from the major tributaries (Hitchon and Krouse, 1972). This adds to our hope that the method will be useful throughout the entire watershed. Further progress for this kind of stable isotope "finger-printing" will require that source signals from many more sites be determined. The use of other stable isotopes such as those of nitrogen, although it is much affected by food web fractionation (Hesslein et al., 1991; Peterson and Fry, 1987), or oxygen may improve the specificity of the fingerprint. Other chemical or physiological measurements may also add to the fingerprint.

Very little information is available on the turnover rates of major compositional components of fish such as sulphur, carbon, or nitrogen. Time is certainly an important variable in understanding the change of the isotopic composition of fish flesh in response to a change in food source especially if the fish are migratory. Some of the difficulty in interpreting the data in this study may result from this, i.e., the fish may equilibrate their carbon more rapidly than their sulphur when changing their food source. An exciting possibility would be to compare isotopic composi-tions of different organs within the fish as the turnover times for the elements will differ with the metabolic function of the organ. A kind of assimilation clock may exist in the fish. We have some simple feeding experiments on elemental turnover being concluded in our laboratory at present. The range in equilibration rates for different organs has been demonstrated for carbon in mice (Tieszen et al., 1983). They showed that time to achieve 50% of equilibrium with a new food source varied from 6.4 days in liver to 27.6 days in muscle, and 47.5 days in the brain.

CONCLUSIONS

We have used stable isotopes of sulphur and carbon in fish muscle to demonstrate the highly varied feeding and migration patterns of the broad whitefish in the lower Mackenzie River region. The technique, while not yet explored to its full potential, has exciting possibilities for providing a much more complete understanding of the energy flow through the food webs leading to the productivity of the broad whitefish and other important fish species in the Mackenzie River. It may also be of use in detecting changes in the basic behaviour of the fish in response to human develop-ment impacts in the area. The ability to estimate the food sources of an individual will allow the enhanced interpretation of contaminant body burdens in systems where the technique is applicable.

ACKNOWLEDGEMENTS

We would like to thank R. Hecky, K. Chang-Kue, W. Bond, and J. Reist for reviewing the manuscript and for participating in useful discussions. We also thank M. Koshinsky and her fish processing crew for providing the tissue samples. This work was supported in part by the Northern Oil and Gas Action Plan (NOGAP) project B.3 and regular funding of the Department of Fisheries and Oceans. Support was also received from the Fisheries Joint Management Committee (FJMC).

REFERENCES

BOND, W.A. and R.N. ERICKSON, 1985. Life history studies of anadromous coregonid fishes in two freshwater lake systems on the Tuktoyaktuk Peninsula, Northwest Territories. Canadian Technical Report of Fisheries and Aquatic Sciences No.1336, Western Region, Fisheries and Oceans Canada, Winnipeg, Manitoba, 61 pp.

BUNN, S.E., D.R. BARTON, H.B.N. HYNES, G. POWER, and M.A. POPE, 1989. Stable isotope analysis of carbon flow in a tundra river system. Canadian Journal of Fisheries and Aquatic Sciences, 46(10), 1769-1775

CHANG-KUE, K.T.J. and E.F. JESSOP, 1983. Tracking the movements of adult broad whitefish (*Coregonus nasus*) to their spawning grounds in the Mackenzie River, Northwest Territories. Proceedings, 4th International Conference on Wildlife Biotelemetry, D.G. Pincock (Editor), 22-24 August 1983, Halifax, Nova Scotia, 248-266

DeNIRO, M.J., and S. EPSTEIN, 1978. Influence of diet on the distribution of carbon isotopes in animals. Geochimica et Cosmochimica Acta, 42(5), 495-506

FEE, E.J., R.E. HECKY, S.J. GUILDFORD, C. ANEMA, D. MATHEW, and K. HALLARD, 1988. Phytoplankton primary production and related limnological data for lakes and channels in the Mackenzie Delta and lakes on the Tuktoyaktuk Peninsula, N.W.T. Canadian Technical Report of Fisheries and Aquatic Sciences No.1614, Fisheries and Oceans Canada, Ottawa, Ontario, 62 pp.

HATFIELD, C.T., J.N. STEIN, M.R. FALK, and C.S. JESSOP, 1972a. Fish resources of the Mackenzie River valley, Interim Report 1, Volume I. Fisheries Service, Environment Canada, Winnipeg, Manitoba, 247 pp.

HATFIELD, C.T., J.N. STEIN, M.R. FALK, C.S. JESSOP, and D.N. SHEPHERD, 1972b. Fish resources of the Mackenzie River valley, Interim Report 1, Volume II. Fisheries Service, Environment Canada, Winnipeg, Manitoba, 289 pp.

HESSLEIN, R.H., M.J. CAPEL, D.E. FOX, and K. HALLARD, 1991. Stable isotopes of sulphur, carbon, and nitrogen as indicators of aquatic food web relationships and fish migration in two lakes off the Mackenzie River, (under review)

HESSLEIN, R.H., D.E. FOX, and M.J. CAPEL, 1989. Sulfur, carbon, and nitrogen isotopic composition of fish from the Mackenzie River delta region and other Arctic drainages. Canadian Data Report on Fisheries and Aquatic Sciences No.728, Fisheries and Oceans Canada, 11 pp.

HITCHON, B., and H.R. KROUSE, 1972. Hydrogeochemistry of the surface waters of the Mackenzie River drainage basin, Canada - III. Stable isotopes of oxygen, carbon, and sulphur. Geochimica and Cosmochimica Acta, 36(12), 1337-1357

PERCY, R., 1975. Fishes of the outer Mackenzie Delta. Beaufort Sea Technical Report No.8, Beaufort Sea Project, Department of the Environment, Victoria, British Columbia, 114 pp.

PETERSON, B.J. and B. FRY, 1987. Stable isotopes in ecosystem studies. Annual Review of Ecology and Systematics, Vol.18, 293-320

REIST, J.D., 1987. Western arctic fish collections 1983-1986: sample-processing procedures and basic data on individual specimens. Canadian Data Report on Fisheries and Aquatic Sciences No.669, Fisheries and Oceans Canada, 69 pp.

REIST, J.D., and W.A. BOND, 1988. Life history characteristics of migratory coregonids of the lower Mackenzie River, Northwest Territories, Canada. Finnish Fisheries Research, Vol.9, 133-144

SCHELL, D.M., 1983. Carbon-13 and Carbon-14 abundances in Alaskan aquatic organisms: delayed production from peat in arctic food webs. Science, 219(4588), 1068-1071

STEIN, J.N., C.S. JESSOP, T.R. PORTER and K.T.J. CHANG-KUE, 1973. Fish resources of the Mackenzie River valley: interim report II. Fisheries Service, Department of the Environment, Winnipeg, Manitoba, for the Environmental-Social Program, Northern Pipelines, Ottawa, Ontario, July, 260 pp.

TIESZEN, L.L., T.W. BOUTTON, K.G. TESDAHL and N.A. SLADE, 1983. Fractionation and turnover of stable carbon isotopes in animal tissues: implications for δ^{13}C analysis of diet. Oecologica, 57(1-2), 32-37

ENVIRONMENTAL CHANGE

IMPACT ASSESSMENT OF A COMPLEX ECOSYSTEM - THE MACKENZIE DELTA

S.P. Wilkins[1] and S.M. Hirst[2]

[1]Sigma Engineering Limited
800 - 1176 West Georgia Street
Vancouver, British Columbia
V6E 4A2   CANADA

[2]Allied Ecology Consultants Limited
1071 Hendecourt Road
North Vancouver, British Columbia
V7K 2X3   CANADA

ABSTRACT

Impact assessment traditionally compartmentalizes a proposed project into scientific disciplines, and conducts inventory and assessment studies on each subject. The study design is often developed by individual discipline specialists without consultation with other scientists, and the necessity for an integrated sampling program is not recognized. An attempt was made to avoid this error in the design of Mackenzie Delta studies for B.C. Hydro's assessment of the impacts of proposed hydro-electric development of the Liard River. From the conception of these studies, it was recognized that the Delta was a complex, interactive ecosystem, and that study integration was essential. The Delta was conceptualized as a dynamic wetland with key physical driving processes, and a system of classification of morphological/ ecological units, terrestrial vegetation types, and hydrological regime/lake types was developed which permitted systematic sampling and analysis.

Within this framework, over four years of detailed studies were conducted on numerous disciplines resulting in nearly forty reports on the Mackenzie Delta. However, an overall synthesis and impact assessment was never written, due to suspension of all engineering and environmental feasibility studies on the proposed Liard River hydro-electric project in 1984. In an attempt to conduct some of this analysis and summarize all of the data collected by the B.C. Hydro studies, an unsolicited proposal by part of the former B.C. Hydro study team was presented to the appropriate federal agencies. This synthesis developed the most comprehensive conceptual model of the delta ecosystem to date, conducted various quantitative analyses of the relationships between physical and biological components, and identified remaining data gaps (Hirst et al., 1987).

A more complete description of the delta ecosystem than that attempted by the B.C. Hydro studies has yet to be undertaken. However, an adaptable working model of the delta ecosystem should remain a research priority for the appropriate government agencies, to provide a framework for future research and development of this complex ecosystem.

INTRODUCTION

The Mackenzie Delta represents one of the most studied regions of Arctic Canada, but it has rarely been considered on an entire ecosystem basis. Given the immensity of the 13,500 km^2 Delta, this is perhaps understandable as researchers have limited their studies to restricted geographical portions of the Delta, selected processes or selected components of the ecosystem. The deltaic ecosystem is relatively simple when compared to the species diversity and complexity of an ecosystem such as a tropical rainforest, but it still represents an interactive, multi-disciplinary study which is beyond the scope, expertise and mandate of many researchers and agencies. However, for the purposes of impact assessment of upstream hydro-electric development, consideration of the impacts on the entire ecosystem was considered essential.

B.C. Hydro's studies of the potential impacts of the proposed Liard Hydro-electric Project in Northern B.C. conducted from 1978 to 1984 was probably the largest scale attempt to study the entire Mackenzie Delta ecosystem to date. This study represented B.C. Hydro's first major initiative in ecosystem-based impact assessment. It was also unprecedented for B.C. Hydro to consider the impacts of a project 1700-km upstream of the Delta, but the potential for significant impacts warranted the large study effort. Despite the seeming wealth of information on various aspects of the Delta, major data gaps existed and no attempt had ever been made to assess impacts of a major project on the entire Delta. The only other major project which was assessed for its impacts on the Delta was the gas pipeline crossings, which were much more site specific.

The study design rationale, a brief summary of the techniques and results of some of the nearly forty individual study components, and some of the lessons learned during the five-year duration of the project are presented. Most of this information has been abstracted from a detailed report summarizing and synthesizing the results of B.C. Hydro's studies in the Delta (Hirst *et al.*, 1987). The intent is that this framework and some of the data may be of value to other researchers attempting to study the Mackenzie Delta ecosystem, either in whole or in part.

IMPACT ASSESSMENT STUDY DESIGN

The traditional approach to impact assessment was to compartmentalize a proposed project into scientific disciplines, and conduct inventory and assessment studies on each individual subject. The study design was often developed by individual discipline specialists without consultation with other scientists, and the necessity for an integrated sampling program was not recognized. The unfortunate field of "helicopter ecology" (Hilborn and Walters, 1981) was born, and a lot of money was spent on inventories and species checklists in the name of impact assessment. Ten years later the situation has improved considerably, but the new profession of "spreadsheet biologist" continues to amass data without providing much more than a general qualitative description of the perceived impacts of any given development.

Ecosystem-based impact assessment has been advocated since the mid-seventies, most notably by authors such as Holling (1978), Hilborn and Walters (1981), and Walters (1986). Environmental assessments can be classified into three types of studies: baseline, processes, and case studies. Long-term baseline studies have long been considered essential to understand the unperturbed natural system and to establish the range of natural variability. Process studies on the other hand utilize experimental methods to understand the behaviour of components of the ecosystem, and the results from one study area can be applied in other areas. However, there are often difficulties in applying studies from laboratory-scale to real-world settings, and from one geographical area to another. Similarly, selection of the "key" processes to be studied from the many which operate within an ecosystem can be a difficult decision at the initiation of a study. Cause and effect in a multivariate system is often difficult to determine without several years of exploratory study. Case studies can be very valuable indicators of potential impacts, particularly if pre-development data and post-development monitoring are available. However, to be scientifically rigorous, controls are essential, which represents a major increase in cost.

The 1980s saw a large increase in the use of computer simulation models in an attempt to synthesize process studies and baseline data (Hilborn and Walters, 1981). Mathematical models of various ecological processes, particularly aquatic systems, have been developed for numerous examples over the past twenty years (e.g., Park, 1974; Sullivan *et al.*, 1983). Conceptual and qualitative rule-based models (e.g., Starfield *et al.*, 1989a, 1989b) continue to play a valuable role in ecosystem prediction where insufficient data are available for quantitative models.

B.C. HYDRO STUDIES IN THE MACKENZIE DELTA

In 1978, B.C. Hydro commenced engineering and environmental feasibility studies on the possible hydro-electric development of the Liard River, a major tributary of the Mackenzie River. Initial hydrology studies indicated that regulation of the Liard could result in the order of a 20 to 30 percent reduction in the Mackenzie River flow at the Delta, which prompted a detailed investigation of the possible downstream impacts of the project. Detailed studies on the Delta commenced in 1979, and continued until 1983 when B.C. Hydro discontinued all investigations of the proposed Liard hydro-electric project.

At the initiation of the B.C. Hydro studies, a preliminary review of data available on the Mackenzie Delta was conducted, and revealed several in-depth studies on topics ranging from waterfowl (Porsild, 1935) to muskrats (Hawley and Hawley, 1963) to geomorphology (Mackay, 1963; Lewis, 1988) to permafrost (Smith, 1973, 1976). However, these studies had all been conducted independently and their data could not be integrated. The studies by Gill (1971a, 1971b, 1972, 1975) concentrated on one study area and probably came the closest of all investigators to date in utilizing an ecosystem approach. Baseline data on plant communities were mapped by Gill and the physical processes determining the distribution of plant communities were investigated. Fisheries studies conducted in the mid-1970s to assess the possible impacts of proposed oil and gas development (Hatfield *et al.*, 1972; Stein *et al.*, 1973; de Graaf and Machniak, 1977) represented the most thorough investigation of impacts of a proposed development on the Delta prior to 1980.

To address the concerns about impact-assessment study design, an interactive, multi-disciplinary workshop was held early in B.C. Hydro's Mackenzie Delta study planning process (Jones *et al.*, 1980). This workshop brought together scientists with specific Mackenzie Delta experience, and planners and simulation modellers with expertise in the design of impact assessments. Despite the effort being hampered by a lack of baseline data for most disciplines, a study design was subsequently developed which formed the framework for further studies.

An essential feature of the study design was to devise a method to spatially sample and subsample the entire Delta, prior to any new data collection. This was accomplished by subdividing the Delta based on its hydrological regime and geomorphological characteristics (Blachut *et al.*, 1985), and seven study areas within those areas were selected for further study (Figure 1). Aerial photography of the Delta was flown for the four transects shown on Figure 1, during the late summer low-flow period in 1980, and during spring flood from 1980 to 1983. The transects sampled with this photography were estimated to cover 2,000 km^2, or 15% of the total delta area. Areas of 5,067 lakes (representing 21% of the estimated 24,000 lakes) were mapped at both low water and under spring flood conditions for several years (Blachut *et al.*, 1985). The lakes were then classified as to their hydrological characteristics (Figure 2), and extent of flooding for each of three years was measured. Water-level data were also collected using time-lapse recorder cameras in each of the study areas and at various other locations within the delta, both by the B.C. Hydro studies (Blachut *et al.*, 1985) and by the National Hydrology Research Institute (Bigras, 1985, 1986; Marsh, 1985). An anticipated quantitative relationship between peak water levels and maximum extent of area flooding was not found, but its absence was attributed to the short period of record rather than flawed conceptual reasoning. The highly-discontinuous spatial and temporal behaviour of the ice regime and its influence on peak water levels and spatial extent of flooding was revealed through observations of the ice and temperature regimes of lakes and channels. Additional survey work, including inertial surveys for the B.C. Hydro study areas, was conducted, resulting in a physical data base and framework for assessment of impacts of flow regulation. All other physical and biological studies focussed on the same sites to the maximum extent possible, to permit eventual integration of physical and biological assessment. The approach also forced numerous interdisciplinary discussions and transfer of data sets to take place as part of the study design process.

Detailed sediment studies were never conducted as part of the B.C. Hydro program, but indirect analysis of sediment distribution was obtained during the

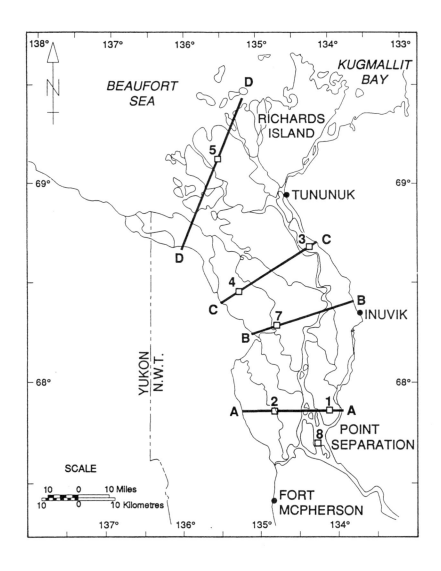

Figure 1.   Position of aerial transects and study areas used for B.C. Hydro environmental studies, 1980 to 1983.

Wilkins and Hirst

LAKE TYPE	DEFINITION	SUBTYPES	CRITERIA FOR AIR PHOTO INTERPRETATION
NO CLOSURE (A)	A lake connected to a distributary for entire open water season; a lake with no closure from the river	* near/far from distributary * position in a chain of lakes * throughflow lakes * genetic types: floodplain, thermokarst, etc.	* presence of flowing connecting channel on late summer photography * inundated during break up flood
LOW CLOSURE (B)	A lake with low closure from the river system; a lake which floods annually but loses its connection during the open water season	* near/far from distributary * position in a chain of lakes * quantitative spill elevation classes * genetic types: floodplain, thermokarst, etc.	* no connection visible on late summer photography * inundated during annual break up flood
HIGH CLOSURE (C)	A lake with high closure from the river system; floods infrequently, or less than annually	* near/far from distributary * position in a chain of lakes * quantitative spill elevation classes * genetic types: floodplain, thermokarst, etc. * quantitative flood frequency classes	* no connection visible on late summer photography * inundated only under high break up flood

(1) from Blachut et al, 1985

Figure 2. Mackenzie Delta lake classification.

vegetation studies (Cordes *et al.*, 1984) and a lake sedimentation survey (Cordes and McLennan, 1984c). Amount of sedimentation appears to be a significant determinant of habitat distribution, and as it could be potentially impacted by regulation, it should be studied as an integral part of any future studies.

The Delta was conceptualized as a dynamic wetland consisting of a sedimentary substrate subjected to four major physical regimes - climatic, thermal, water flow and sediments/water quality (Figure 3). The action of the processes results in a complex mosaic of terrestrial and aquatic habitats which are defined by their physical structure. Biological populations occupying these habitats include the autotrophic primary-producer communities of terrestrial vegetation, aquatic macrophytes, benthic algae and phytoplankton, and the heterotrophic secondary-producer communities of wildlife, fish and invertebrates. The major driving physical forces act not only on the delta surface but also directly on the biological populations. The delta surface was differentiated into morphological/ecological units and sub-units (Figure 4) based on an ecological classification scheme (Cordes *et al.*, 1984). The four basic geomorphological units of the delta surface were channels, basins, delta plain and pingos. Terrestrial vegetation was then further subdivided into ecological phases which occur as successional sequences within the sub-units (Figure 5).

Various physical parameters were measured at representative sites within the study areas, in an attempt to establish process-response relationships between physical variables and vegetation (Cordes *et al.*, 1984). A compilation of these data and the analyses to test for statistical significance of relationships were conducted by Hirst *et al.* (1987). Relationships between ecological types and sedimentation rates, annual flooding duration, soil texture, depth to water-table and depth to permafrost, drainage, organic-matter content and soil chemistry were all tested. The sub-types were found to represent units of relatively homogeneous characteristics such as morphology, hydrological regime, soil type, vegetation chronosequences and other features. Similarly, relationships between the ecological phases and physical parameters were also explored, and the three major categories of determinants were found to be climate, flooding regime and substrate. These relationships, the succession between phases and the potential impact of flow alteration on succession were all explored in detail by Cordes *et al.* (1984), Pearce and Cordes (1985) and Pearce (1986). Relationships between additional determinants such as climate and the ecology of delta vegetation were also explored (Cordes and McLennan, 1984d; Hirst, 1982), to determine if break-up affects the delta mesoclimate sufficiently to alter the timing of bud-burst.

Aquatic ecological studies for B.C. Hydro (Hatfield, 1981; Taylor *et al.*, 1982) were integrated into the delta conceptual ecological model through the hydrological classification scheme developed by B.C. Hydro (Blachut *et al.*, 1985). The various lake and channel types were treated as the aquatic equivalents of ecological sub-types in the interpretation of aquatic habitat, and the impacts of the proposed project were assessed on that basis. The hydrological classification was extended by Hirst *et al.* (1987) to ensure uniformity with the terrestrial classification system and to ensure that the entire delta surface was represented in the delta model.

Wilkins and Hirst

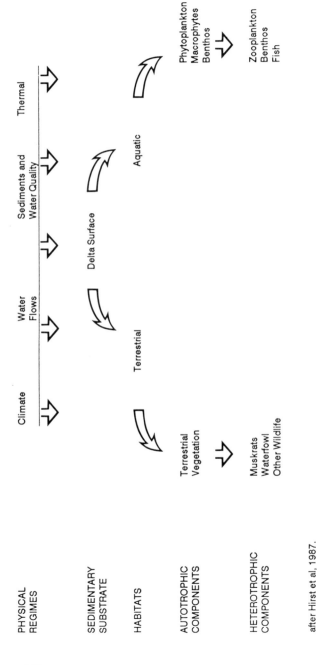

Figure 3. Conceptual model of the components of the Mackenzie Delta.

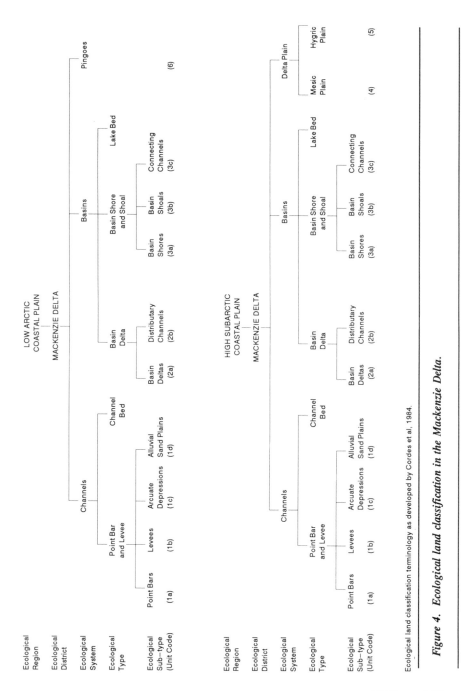

Ecological land classification terminology as developed by Cordes et al, 1984.

Figure 4. Ecological land classification in the Mackenzie Delta.

141

Wilkins and Hirst

ECOLOGICAL REGION	High Subarctic Coastal Plain									Delta Plain		
ECOLOGICAL SYSTEM	Channels					Basins						
ECOLOGICAL TYPE	Point Bar and Levee				Channel Bed	Basin Delta		Basin Shore and Shoal			Lake Bed	Mesic Plain	Hydric Plain
ECOLOGICAL SUB-TYPE	Point Bars	Levees	Arcuate Depressions	Alluvial Sand Plains		Basin Deltas	Distributary Channels	Basin Shores	Basin Shoals	Connecting Channels			
ECOLOGICAL PHASE	Mudflats; Equisetum; Salix –; Equisetum; Salix; Alnus – Salix; Populus; Picea	Cutbanks; Mudflats; Equisetum; Carex; Salix – Carex; Salix –; Equisetum; Salix; Alnus – Salix; Populus; Picea	Carex; Salix –; Carex; Picea	Mudflats; Sandflats; Salix –; Equisetum; Salix; Alnus – Salix; Populus		Mudflats; Equisetum; Arctophila; Carex; Salix – Carex	Cutbanks; Mudflats; Equisetum; Carex; Salix –; Equisetum; Salix; Alnus – Salix; Populus; Picea	Mudflats; Equisetum; Carex; Salix – Carex; Salix; Alnus – Salix; Picea	Mudflats; Equisetum; Arctophila; Carex; Salix – Carex	Mudflats; Equisetum; Carex; Salix –; Equisetum; Salix; Alnus – Salix; Picea		Alnus – Salix; Picea	Picea

Classification developed by Cordes et al (1984), modified by C.M. Pearce

Figure 5. Terrestrial ecological phases of the Mackenzie Delta.

The water chemistry of selected lakes within the B.C. Hydro study areas was sampled (Hatfield, 1981; Taylor *et al.*, 1982), providing data on nutrients, temperature, total suspended solids, light-extinction coefficient, dissolved oxygen, pH and conductivity. Measures of primary and secondary aquatic productivity, including chlorophyll-a, phytoplankton, aquatic macrophytes, zooplankton, and zoobenthos were investigated (Hatfield, 1981; Taylor *et al.*, 1982; Cordes and McLennan, 1984b). Fish population, abundance and distribution and limits to fish productivity in delta lakes were evaluated (Hatfield, 1981; Taylor *et al.*, 1982; Hirst *et al.*, 1987).

While numerous large mammal, fur-bearer and bird species are included in the delta ecosystem, two dominant species - muskrats and waterfowl - were selected for the B.C. Hydro investigations. These two groups were also seen to have their habitat requirements potentially very closely linked to changes in flow regime, and hence be at the greatest risk of being impacted by flow regulation. Studies on muskrat ecology were conducted in four of the seven B.C. Hydro study areas, including population estimates, habitat requirements and food sources (Welch *et al.*, 1984; McCourt, 1985). Waterfowl were studied in 1982 and 1983, including census and estimates of population, distribution of birds within study areas, habitat requirements, and the relationship between waterfowl populations and various hydrological variables (Alliston, 1984; Alliston, 1985; Hirst *et al.*, 1987).

Several other studies were conducted as part of the overall B.C. Hydro study, and others were proposed which were never initiated. A list of all the individual reports prepared under this program is included in Appendix I. Copies of these reports are held in Vancouver by B.C. Hydro and at the Boreal Institute library, Edmonton, Alberta. An important initiative to collate and synthesize the results of these studies was undertaken subsequent to the B.C. Hydro program (Hirst *et al.*, 1987), and will be discussed further below.

ANALYSIS OF THE MACKENZIE DELTA ECOSYSTEM

Following the collection of several years of data, a subsequent series of workshops were held by B.C. Hydro to attempt to integrate the data from various disciplines, using a numerical simulation model as the framework (Everitt *et al.*, 1982). The models and workshop served several purposes; integration of existing data, identification of data gaps, extrapolation of results from individual study areas to the entire Delta, and the opportunity to permit input from regulatory agencies to the study process. The models, while moving from the conceptual to numerical simulation, still were limited by data gaps and critical assumptions which must be made. Moving into the socio-economic sub-model proved particularly difficult, as the feedback loop between the impacts on the biophysical resources of the Delta and the local populations, and value judgements of those impacts were unknown.

B.C. Hydro-sponsored studies of the delta ecosystem were terminated prior to any synthesis of the data. Environment Canada funded an unsolicited proposal from a group of former B.C. Hydro employees to prepare such a report, with permission from B.C. Hydro to use all the relevant data and background reports. That report (Hirst *et al.*, 1987) does not explicitly address the impacts of hydro-electric development on the Delta, but is a detailed analysis of the delta ecosystem as it was understood at the conclusion of the B.C. Hydro studies.

To organize the large amount of data collected, some consistent terminology was utilized to describe elements of the ecosystem (Figure 3). Two parameters were defined for each basic habitat; habitat determinants and habitat characteristics. A determinant is defined as a feature or process which is essential for the development or maintenance of an ecological type, sub-type or phase as suitable habitat. Examples are the high flooding frequency responsible for the continued existence of an early successional species such as Equisetum, or a flow connection between a lake and the channel system to permit fish access to the lake. A characteristic is a feature by which a type, sub-type or phase can be recognized, differentiated, classified and sometimes mapped. Some characteristics are states such as silt content of a sediment deposit, while others are processes such as sedimentation rates. For each major component of the ecosystem, matrices were compiled to summarize the existing understanding of the determinants of habitat and habitat characteristics. These figures were completed to the maximum extent possible, but in many cases data gaps were revealed, as indicated in the attached examples (Figures 6 and 7). The matrices then provided the basis for some quantification and hypothesis testing of the relationships between variables. Four types of analysis were undertaken, depending on the particular hypothesis and the available data: simulation modelling, statistical comparisons using parametric and non-parametric tests, cumulative departures from the mean in long-term time-series data, and quantitative descriptions using comparative statistics. A further attempt at quantitative analysis of the delta ecosystem was attempted by Hirst *et al.* (1987; Appendix F), with a simulation model of a delta-lake ecosystem. Using the data base available, system equations were derived for eight interlinked sub-models, including water volume, energy, sedimentation, phosphorous, nitrogen, phytoplankton, food chain, and detritus, and included 60 input parameters and 127 output variables. Calibration of the various sub-models revealed that several of the physical variables could be quite accurately modelled, while others, particularly nutrients and primary production, achieved poor results. Sensitivity analysis was tested by changing the input variables, while other techniques were suggested for further work.

One of the main conclusions reached by the Hirst *et al.* (1987) study was that the stability of an ecosystem and its response to change is the key to conducting impact assessment. Stability is described as an inherent characteristic of an ecosystem and is defined by Holling (1973) as the ability to return to an equilibrium state after a temporary disturbance. However to determine ecosystem stability presumes a sufficient data base to test that stability over time. The other measure of the health of an ecosystem is resilience, the ability of an ecosystem to absorb changes and still persist (Holling, 1973). The physical ecosystem determinants and the response of biota to changes in those parameters can be used as a test of their importance in ecosystem maintenance and stability. An example is the control exerted on muskrat

Wilkins and Hirst

HABITAT COMPONENTS	DETERMINANTS	NESTING HABITAT			BROODING HABITAT			NON- AND POST-BREEDING HABITAT			SPRING STAGING HABITAT					FALL STAGING HABITAT		
		DABBLERS	DIVERS	SWANS	DABBLERS	DIVERS	SWANS	DABBLERS	DIVERS	SWANS	DABBLERS	DIVERS	SWANS	SNOW GEESE	DARK GEESE	DABBLERS	DIVERS	SWANS
Hydrology	Latest date for open water availability on channels and lakes	--	--	--	--	--	--	--	--	--	June 7	June 7	June 7	--	--	--	--	--
	Latest date for exposure of shoreline mudflats	--	--	--	--	--	--	--	--	--	--	--	June 7	May 30	May 30	--	--	--
	Latest date for exposure of shoreline emergents and nest material	June 25 (mallard, pintail), June 30 (others)	June 15 (golden-eye) June 25 (canvasback, scoters) July 11 (scaups)	June 15	--	--	--	--	--	--	--	--	--	--	--	--	--	--
	Maximum sediment deposition on shoreline emergent vegetation (cm)	10	10	--	--	--	--	--	--	--	--	--	--	--	--	--	--	--
	Maximum daily water level fluctuations (m)	0.1	0.3	0.5	0.5	0.5	0.5	--	--	--	--	--	--	--	--	--	--	--
	Water velocity	Minimal	Minimal	Minimal	Low	Low	Low	Low	Low	Low	Low	Low	Low	Low	Low	Low	Low	Low
	Minimum water depth (cm)	--	10	--	10	30	30	10	30	30	10	30	30	--	--	10	30	30
	Maximum suspended sediment concentration (mg/l)	--	--	--	10	10	10	--	10	10	10	10	--	--	--	--	10	--
Geomorphology	Maximum shoreline slope (degrees)	20	--	--	20	20	20	--	--	--	--	--	20	20	20	--	--	--
	Minimum size of water body (ha)	0.05	0.05	50	--	--	--	--	--	50	--	--	--	--	--	--	--	50
Nesting and Protective Cover	Minimum width of shoreline emergent zone (m)	1	1	--	1	1	1	--	--	--	--	--	10	10	10	--	--	--
	Maximum woody vegetation canopy cover (%)	50	50	50	--	--	--	--	--	--	--	--	--	--	--	--	--	--
Food Resources	Abundant macrophytes required	No	No	No	Yes	Yes	Yes	Yes	Yes	Yes	Yes	Yes	Yes	No	No	Yes	Yes	Yes
	Abundant zooplankton and zoobenthos required	No	No	No	Yes	Yes	Yes	No	Yes	No	Yes	No	No	No	No	No	Yes	No

Figure 6. Determinant matrix for waterfowl in the Mackenzie Delta.

A. LAND SURFACE

HABITAT COMPONENTS	CHARACTERISTICS	POINT BAR	LEVEE	ARCUATE DEPRESSION	ALLUVIAL SAND PLAIN	BASIN DELTA	DISTRIBUTARY CHANNEL	BASIN SHORE	BASIN SHOAL	CONNECTING CHANNEL	LAKE CHANNEL	MESIC PLAIN	HYGRIC PLAIN
Hydrology	Shoreline mudflats exposed for spring staging	May 17–30 (Zone A) May 23–30 (others)	-	--	May 17–30 (Zone A)	--	--	--	--	--	--	--	--
	Shoreline emergents exposed for duck nesting	<July 1	<July 1	<June 15	<July 1	<June 15	<1 July	<June 15	<July 1	<1 July	<1 July	--	--
	Sediment deposition on shoreline emergent vegetation (cm)	0.2 – 9.2	0.3 – 10.0	<1.0	0.5 – 10.0	0.1 – 13.0	0	0.2 – 7.0	0.1 – 14.0	0	0	<1.0	<1.0
	Daily water level fluctuations (m)	0 – 1.5	0 – 1.5	0 – 0.5	0 – 1.5	0 – 1.5	0 – 1.5	0 – 1.5	0 – 1.5	0 – 1.5	0 – 1.5	0 – 0.1	0 – 0.1
	Water Velocity	Mod – High	Mod – High	Nil	Mod – High	Low – Mod	Mod – High	Low – Mod	Low – Mod	Mod – High	Nil – High	Nil	Nil
Geomorphology	Shoreline Slope (degrees)	1 – 10	0 – 40	--	--	0 – 2	0 – 15	0 – 5	0 – 5	0 – 15	0 – 15	0 – 2	0 – 2
Nesting and Protective Cover	Width of shoreline emergent zone (m)	0 – 50	0 – 10	0 – 50	0 – 500	20 – 500	0 – 5	10 – 50	0 – 50	0 – 5	0 – 5	0	0
	Woody vegetation canopy cover (%)	0 – 90	0 – 90	5 – 90	0 – 90	0 – 80	0 – 90	0 – 80	0 – 60	0 – 90	0 – 90	50 – 95	40 – 90

B. WATER BODIES

HABITAT COMPONENTS	CHARACTERISTICS	CONNECTED LAKE	INTERMEDIATE CLOSURE LAKE	HIGH CLOSURE LAKE	DISTRIBUTARY CHANNEL	CONNECTING CHANNEL	LAKE CHANNEL
Hydrology	Open water on channels or lakes	May 28 (Zone B) May 28 (Zone C) May 28 (Zone D)	May 23 (Zone A) May 28 (Zone B) May 28 (Zone C) May 28 (Zone D)	May 28 (Zone A) May 28 (Zone B) May 28 (Zone C) June 1 (Zone D)	May 15 (Zone A) May 23 (Zone B) May 23 (Zone C) May 23 (Zone D)	May 15 (Zone A) May 23 (Zone B) May 23 (Zone C) May 28 (Zone D)	May 28 (Zone A) May 28 (Zone B) May 28 (Zone C) May 28 (Zone D)
	Daily water level fluctuations (m)	0 – 1.5	0 – 0.5	0 – 0.1	0 – 1.5	0 – 1.5	0 – 1.5
	Water velocity	Nil – Moderate	Nil – Low	Nil	Low – High	Nil – High	Nil – High
	Suspended sediments (mg/l)	<1 – >1000	<1 – 50	<1 – 8	<1 – >1000	<1 – >1000	<1 – >1000
Geomorphology	Median size of water body (ha)	3.4	2.1	1.1	--	--	--
Food Resources	Macrophyte density (freq, % occurrence)	40 – 90	95 – 100	95 – 100	0	0 – 20	0 – 90
	Zooplankton density (mg/m3)	<0.1 – 70	15 – 200	10 – 115	<10	<10	<10
	Zoobenthos biomass (mg/m2)	<1 – 13	3 – 137	4 – 56	<1	<1	<1

Figure 7. Ecological sub-type habitat characteristics matrix for waterfowl in the Mackenzie Delta.

distribution and survival by the ice thickness on lakes. Despite the lack of an adequate data base, the natural variability of delta components and associated processes was summarized using a quantitative measure known as a maximum-minimum ratio. The preliminary results indicate that a very high degree of variability persists, in both physical factors such as flood frequencies, flood duration and sedimentation rates and biological populations. The tentative conclusion based on these high ratios is that the Delta is highly resilient to natural variability. Whether this resilience, which is in response to typically random or cyclic variation, can be applied to permanent man-made change which is more likely offset or trending is unknown. The man-made change may also induce change beyond an unknown threshold, which could result in rapid and unanticipated change.

These B.C. Hydro-sponsored conceptualizations and analyses of the Mackenzie Delta ecosystem were not without flaws, in part due to their focus on impacts of upstream hydro-electric development. Study areas and target species selection was driven by potential for impact by upstream regulation or economic value. Permafrost was not considered, nor song birds or moose. The range of predicted flow changes due to regulation was within the range of long-term natural variability, making the impacts appear to be subtle and difficult to demonstrate their significance. However, in its favour, a deltaic ecosystem is primarily determined by its hydrological regime, which was by necessity the focus of the B.C. Hydro studies. The issue of cumulative impacts of upriver development on the Delta was recognized as a potential issue, but not addressed by the B.C. Hydro studies.

The lessons learned on the topic of ecosystem modelling were many; in Canadian environmental studies, it is rare that such a large data set has been amassed and analyzed on an entire delta ecosystem. The conventional engineering wisdom that the impacts of regulating the annual peak flow will have minimal environmental effects is contradicted by the results of this study. As postulated by scientists such as Odum, a delta represents a pulse-stabilized ecosystem and is dependent on the spring peak flood to maintain the primary successional vegetation communities that in turn provide the rich wildlife habitat (Odum, 1971). The complexity of inter-relationships between components of the ecosystem and their physical determinants indicates that impacts of development are not likely to be simple, linear or unidirectional, and potential synergistic effects of ecosystem alteration will have to be considered. The high degree of natural variability experienced in the parameters measured on the Mackenzie Delta indicates that a sufficiently large data base is essential to adequately assess the impacts of any proposed development on the stability and resilience of the delta ecosystem.

RECOMMENDATIONS AND CONCLUSIONS

The present state of knowledge of the Mackenzie Delta ecosystems and their behaviour is still inadequate to accurately predict changes in key processes and driving forces. The high degree of natural variability observed is apparently inherent in deltaic ecology. The most significant research needs identified by the ecosystem synthesis study (Hirst *et al.*, 1987) are: the hydrodynamics of flow distribution throughout the delta, hydrodynamics of annual and seasonal flooding, sediment transport and distribution, microclimate within the Delta and the relationship to river heat inputs, nutrient, macrophytes, detritus and food-chain dynamics within delta lakes, the use of delta channels as overwintering fish habitat, long-term trends in vegetation succession, long-term trends in muskrat population abundance, and long-term trends in waterfowl abundance and production.

A more complete description of the delta ecosystem than that attempted by the B.C. Hydro studies has yet to be undertaken. It will perhaps have to be undertaken in an academic or agency milieu, as the studies conducted by proponents of development will likely be influenced by the need to address their anticipated impacts. The potential for multiple types of development affecting the Delta, such as other upriver hydro-electric projects (i.e., Slave River and Great Bear Lake), offshore oil and gas, and transportation corridors will make a comprehensive model essential to assess cumulative impacts. Superimposed on the man-made impacts, natural variation and finally macroscale man-induced changes such as climate change further complicate the problem. The final layer of complexity is added by potential socio-economic impacts of development, which was not addressed by either the B.C. Hydro or Hirst *et al.* (1987) studies. This deliberate decision by B.C. Hydro was predicated on the assumption that bio-physical impacts would need to be estimated to enable socio-economic impact assessment studies to be designed. However, future studies which intend to predict the total impact of development on the Delta will have to incorporate socio-economic concerns with the biophysical.

Laudable efforts continue to be made by several agencies (Water Survey of Canada, Inland Waters Branch, National Hydrology Research Institute, Canadian Wildlife Service) to continue to extend the data base on selected variables, and to increase the understanding of various processes and interactions. However, an adaptable working model of the delta ecosystem should remain a research priority for the appropriate government agencies, to provide a framework for future research and development of this incredibly complex ecosystem.

REFERENCES

Any B.C. HYDRO reports referred to in the text of the paper are listed in Appendix I.

BIGRAS, S.C., 1985. Lake regimes, Mackenzie Delta, N.W.T., 1981. Internal report, Cold Regions Section, Surface Water Division, National Hydrology Research Institute, Ottawa, Ontario, February, 39 pp.

BIGRAS, S.C., 1986. Lake regimes, Mackenzie Delta, N.W.T., 1982 and 1983. Internal Report, Surface Water Division, National Hydrology Research Institute, Environment Canada, Ottawa, Ontario, 63 pp.

de GRAAF, D. and K. MACHNIAK, 1977. Fisheries investigations along the cross delta pipeline route in the Mackenzie delta. In - Studies to Determine the Impact of Gas Pipeline

Development on Aquatic Ecosystems, P. McCart (Editor), Arctic Gas Biology Report Series No.39, 169 pp.

GILL, D., 1971a. Vegetation and environment in the Mackenzie River Delta, N.W.T.: a study in subarctic ecology. Ph.D. thesis, Department of Geography, University of British Columbia, Vancouver, British Columbia, 694 pp.

GILL, D., 1971b. Damming the Mackenzie: a theoretical assessment of the long-term influence of river impoundment on the ecology of the Mackenzie River delta. Proceedings, Peace Athabasca Delta Symposium, E.R. Reinelt et al. (Editors), 14-15 January 1971, University of Alberta, Edmonton, Alberta, May, 204-222

GILL, D., 1972. The point bar environment in the Mackenzie River delta. Canadian Journal of Earth Sciences, 9(11), 1382-1391

GILL, D., 1975. Significance of spring break-up to the bioclimate of the Mackenzie River delta. In - The Coast and Shelf of the Beaufort Sea, J.C. Reed and J.E. Slater (Editors), Arctic Institute of North America, Montréal, Quebec, 543-544

HATFIELD, C.T., J.N. STEIN, M.R. FALK and C.S. JESSOP, 1972. Fish resources of the Mackenzie River valley, Interim Report 1, Volume I. Fisheries Service, Environment Canada, Winnipeg, Manitoba, 247 pp.

HAWLEY, V.D. and L.A. HAWLEY, 1963. Muskrat management studies in the Mackenzie Delta: Annual Progress Report, 1962-63, Project M3-2-1. Unpublished report, Canadian Wildlife Service, Ottawa, Ontario, 37 pp.

HILBORN, R. and C.J. WALTERS, 1981. Pitfalls of environmental baseline and process studies. Environmental Impact Assessment Review, 2(3), 265-278

HIRST, S.M., M. MILES, S.P. BLACHUT, L.A. GOULET, and R.E. TAYLOR, 1987. Quantitative synthesis of the Mackenzie Delta ecosystems. Applied Ecology Ltd., North Vancouver, B.C. for Inland Waters Directorate, Western and Northern Region, Conservation and Protection, Environment Canada, Edmonton, Alberta, December, main volume, 407 pp.; appendices, 141 pp.

HOLLING, C.S., 1973. Resilience and stability of ecological systems. Annual Review of Ecological Systematics, Vol.4, 1-23

HOLLING, C.S. (Editor), 1978. Adaptive environmental assessment and management. International Series on Applied Systems Analysis No.3, John Wiley and Sons, New York, 377 pp.

LEWIS, C.P., 1988. Mackenzie Delta sedimentary environments and processes. Draft Contract Report to Sediment Survey Section, Water Resources Branch, Inland Waters Directorate, Environment Canada, Ottawa, Ontario, January 26, 395 pp.

MACKAY, J.R., 1963. The Mackenzie Delta area, N.W.T. Geographical Branch Memoir No.8, Department of Mines and Technical Surveys, Ottawa, Ontario, 202 pp.

MARSH, P., 1985. Mackenzie Delta, lake hydrology progress report. NHRI Internal report, National Hydrology Research Institute, Environment Canada, Ottawa, Ontario, 28 pp.

ODUM, E.P., 1971. Fundamentals of ecology. W.B. Saunders Co. Ltd., Philadelphia, 574 pp.

PARK, R.A., 1974. A generalized model for simulating lake ecosystems. Simulation, 23(2), 33-50

PEARCE, C.M., 1986. The distribution and ecology of the shoreline vegetation on the Mackenzie Delta, N.W.T. Ph.D. thesis, Department of Geography, University of Calgary, Calgary, Alberta, 400 pp.

PORSILD, A.E., 1935. The Mackenzie Delta as a breeding ground for waterfowl. 21st Proceedings, American Game Conference, New York, 283-290

SMITH, M.W., 1973. Factors affecting the distribution of permafrost, Mackenzie Delta, N.W.T. Ph.D. thesis, Department of Geography, University of British Columbia, Vancouver, B.C., 186 pp.

SMITH, M.W., 1976. Permafrost in the Mackenzie Delta, Northwest Territories. Geological Survey of Canada Paper No.75-28, Ottawa, Ontario, 34 pp.

STARFIELD, A.M., B.P. FARM and R.H. TAYLOR, 1989a. A rule-based ecological model for the management of an estuarine lake. Ecological Modelling, 46(1-2), 107-119

STARFIELD, A.M., R.H. TAYLOR, and L.S.SHEN, 1989b. Rule-based models at the interface between engineering and ecology. In - Computing in Civil Engineering, T.O. Barnwell Jr. (Editor), Proceedings, 6th Conference on Computers and Engineering Practice, 11-13 September, 1989, Atlanta, Georgia, American Society of Civil Engineers, Washington, D.C., 154-161

STEIN, J.N., C.S. JESSOP, T.R. PORTER and K.T.J. CHANG-KUE, 1973. Fish resources of the Mackenzie River valley, interim report II. Fisheries Service, Department of the Environment, Winnipeg, Manitoba, for the Environmental-Social Program, Northern Pipelines, Ottawa, Ontario, July, 260 pp.

SULLIVAN, P., G.L. SWARTMAN and H. BINDEMAN, 1983. Processes notebook for aquatic ecosystem simulations. Report No. NUREG/CR-3392, U.S. Nuclear Regulatory Commission, Washington, D.C.

WALTERS, C.J., 1986. Adaptive management of renewable resources. MacMillan, New York, N.Y., 374 pp.

APPENDIX I: *B.C. HYDRO MACKENZIE DELTA STUDIES*

The following bibliography lists all environmental study reports produced for or by B.C. Hydro from 1978 to 1985 which deal with the Mackenzie Delta. Copies of the reports are available through the Boreal Institute, University of Alberta, Edmonton, Alberta or the Environmental Resources Division, B.C. Hydro, Vancouver, B.C.

ALLISTON, W.G., 1984. A study of the numbers, distribution, habitat use and productivity of breeding waterfowl populations in the Mackenzie Delta, summer, 1982. Report by LGL Ltd. for B.C. Hydro, Vancouver, B.C.

ALLISTON, W.G., 1985. A monitoring study of the species, numbers, habitat use and productivity of waterfowl populations on two study areas in the wooded Mackenzie Delta, summer, 1983. B.C. Hydro Liard Hydroelectric Project Studies, Report by LGL Ltd., King City, Ontario for B.C. Hydro, Vancouver, B.C., 83 pp.

AU YEUNG, L., 1983. Liard River hydro-electric development: preliminary downstream socio-economic study. B.C. Hydro Liard Hydroelectric Project Studies, Report ESS-50, Environmental and Socio-Economic Services Department, B.C. Hydro, Vancouver, B.C., 1 volume

B.C. HYDRO., 1980. Environmental assessment of hydro-electric development on the Liard River, B.C., B.C. Hydro Liard Hydroelectric Project Studies, Report ESS-7, Environmental and Socio-Economic Services Department, B.C. Hydro, Vancouver, B.C., 1 volume

B.C. HYDRO., 1982. Liard River hydro-electric development: downstream sediment regime and channel morphology. Report H1281, Hydro-electric Generation Projects Division, B.C. Hydro, Vancouver, B.C.

B.C. HYDRO., 1983. Liard River, Mackenzie River and Mackenzie Delta: ice observations, 1982-83. B.C. Hydro Liard Hydroelectric Project Studies, Report H1650, Hydro-electric Generation Projects Division, B.C. Hydro, Vancouver, B.C., 1 volume

B.C. HYDRO., 1984a. Mackenzie Delta benchmark surveys 1983. Transmission Projects Division, B.C. Hydro, Vancouver, B.C.

B.C. HYDRO., 1984b. Liard River hydro-electric development: downstream water temperature study. Report H1627, Hydro-electric Generation Projects Division, B.C. Hydro, Vancouver, B.C.

B.C. HYDRO., 1985. Liard River hydro-electric development: downstream hydrology. Interim report. B.C. Hydro Liard Hydroelectric Project Studies, Report H1794, Hydro-electric Generation Projects Division, B.C. Hydro, Vancouver, B.C., 1 volume

BLACHUT, S.P., R.E. TAYLOR and S.M. HIRST, 1985. Mackenzie Delta environmental hydrology. B.C. Hydro Liard Hydroelectric Project Studies, Report ESS-92, Hardy Associates (1978) Ltd., Edmonton and Environmental and Socio-Economic Services Department, B.C. Hydro, Vancouver, B.C. 2 volumes

CHURCH, M.A., 1981. Proposed Liard hydro-electric development - a review of environmental studies: sedimentation. Department of Geography, University of British Columbia, Report to B.C. Hydro, Vancouver, B.C.

CORDES, L.D. and D.S. MCLENNAN, 1984a. Bathymetry and morphometry of 32 Mackenzie Delta lakes. B.C. Hydro Liard Hydroelectric Project Studies, Report by L.D. Cordes and Associates, Calgary to B.C. Hydro, Vancouver, B.C., 74 pp.

CORDES, L.D. and D.S. MCLENNAN, 1984b. The distribution of aquatic macrophytes in the lakes of the Mackenzie Delta. B.C. Hydro Liard Hydroelectric Project Studies, Report by L.D. Cordes and Associates, Calgary to B.C. Hydro, Vancouver, B.C., 101 pp.

CORDES, L.D. and D.S. MCLENNAN, 1984c. The estimation of sedimentation rates using ^{137}Cs in the lakes of the Mackenzie Delta. B.C. Hydro Liard Hydroelectric Project Studies, Report by L.D. Cordes and Associates, Calgary to B.C. Hydro, Vancouver, B.C., 68 pp.

CORDES, L.D. and D.S. MCLENNAN, 1984d. Phenology of vegetation in the Mackenzie Delta area - 1981 and 1982. B.C. Hydro Liard Hydroelectric Project Studies, Report by L.D. Cordes and Associates, Calgary to B.C. Hydro, Vancouver, B.C., 168 pp.

CORDES, L.D., D.S. MCLENNAN and C.M. PEARCE, 1984. Alluvial ecosystems in the Mackenzie Delta, N.W.T. B.C. Hydro Liard Hydroelectric Project Studies, Report by L.D. Cordes and Associates, Calgary to B.C. Hydro, Vancouver, B.C., 2 volumes

EALEY, D.M., 1984. Spring migration waterfowl populations along the Mackenzie River and Delta - monitoring 1983. B.C. Hydro Liard Hydroelectric Project Studies, Report from McCourt Management Ltd. to B.C. Hydro, Vancouver, B.C., 98 pp.

EALEY, D.M. and D.F. PENNER, 1983. Spring migrating waterfowl populations along the Mackenzie River and Delta - 1982. B.C. Hydro Liard Hydroelectric Project Studies, Report from McCourt Management Ltd. to B.C. Hydro, Vancouver, B.C., 146 pp.

EVERITT, R.R., P. BUNNELL, A.B. CARRUTHERS, M.L. JONES and N.C. SONNTAG, 1982. Liard River hydro-electric development, application of adaptive environmental assessment and management to planning of the Mackenzie Delta environmental studies. B.C. Hydro Liard Hydroelectric Project Studies, Report by Environmental and Social Systems Analysts Ltd., Vancouver for B.C. Hydro, Vancouver, B.C., 199 pp.

GOULET, L.A., 1985. Muskrat push-up surveys in the Mackenzie Delta - May 1981 and 1982. B.C. Hydro Liard Hydroelectric Project Studies, Report ESS-56, Environmental and Socio-Economic Services Department, B.C. Hydro, Vancouver, B.C., 54 pp.

HARDY ASSOCIATES (1978) LTD., 1982. Alluvial sedimentation of the Mackenzie River system. Report EC-05006, Hardy Associates (1978) Ltd., Edmonton for B.C. Hydro, Vancouver, B.C., 2 volumes

HARRY, K.F. and L.E. PARENT, 1980. Liard River hydro-electric project: a study of climatic effects in the Mackenzie Delta. B.C. Hydro and Power Authority, Vancouver, B.C., 1 volume

HATFIELD CONSULTANTS LTD., 1981. Preliminary impact assessment of the Liard River hydro-electric project on the aquatic productivity of the Mackenzie Delta lakes. Hatfield Consultants Ltd., Vancouver report to B.C. Hydro, Vancouver, B.C., 219 pp.

HIRST, S.M., 1982. Liard River hydro-electric development: effects of flow regulation on microscale air temperatures in the Mackenzie Delta during break-up. Report ESS-18, Environmental and Socio-Economic Services, Engineering Services Division, B.C. Hydro and Power Authority, Vancouver, B.C., 1 volume

HIRST, S.M. and L.A. GOULET, 1982. Liard River hydro-electric development: migratory waterfowl survey of the lower Mackenzie valley, 4 May 1981. Report ESS-48, Environmental and Socio-Economic Services Department, B.C. Hydro, Vancouver, B.C.

HIRST, S.M. and P. ST-PIERRE, 1978. Preliminary environmental assessment of hydro-electric development on the Liard River, B.C. B.C. Hydro Liard Hydroelectric Project Studies, Report SE7802, Environmental Resources Department, B.C. Hydro, Vancouver, B.C., 1 volume

JONES, M.L., R.R. EVERITT, N.C. SONNTAG and M.J. STALEY, 1980. Report on the Liard hydro-electric development, Mackenzie Delta Modelling Workshop. B.C. Hydro Liard Hydroelectric Project Studies, Report by Environmental and Social Systems Analysts Ltd., Vancouver for B.C. Hydro, Vancouver, B.C., 91 pp.

MARKO, J.R., D.B. FISSEL, M.A. WILSON and D. HUSTON, 1983. Background and evaluation of impacts of Liard River hydro-electric development in the southeastern Beaufort Sea. B.C. Hydro Liard Hydroelectric Project Studies, Report by Arctic Sciences Ltd., Sidney to B.C. Hydro, Vancouver, B.C., 1 volume

McCOURT MANAGEMENT LTD., 1985. Studies on muskrat ecology in the Mackenzie Delta, 1983-1984. Report to McCourt Management Limited for Environmental and Socio-Economic Services, B.C. Hydro, Vancouver, B.C., 65 pp.

McELHANNEY SURVEYING and ENGINEERING LTD., 1983. Mackenzie Delta inertial survey. Report to B.C. Hydro, Canadian Wildlife Service and Inland Waters Directorate, Vancouver, B.C.

PARKINSON, F.E. and G.K. HOLDER, 1981. Liard-Mackenzie winter regime study: final report. B.C. Hydro Liard Hydroelectric Project Studies, Report by Lasalle Hydraulic Laboratories to B.C. Hydro, Vancouver, B.C., 3 volumes

PEARCE, C.M. and L.D. CORDES, 1985. Vegetation colonization on the Mackenzie River Delta, 1981-1983. B.C. Hydro Liard Hydroelectric Project Studies, Report by L.D. Cordes and Associates, Calgary to B.C. Hydro, Vancouver, B.C., 381 pp.

SLANEY, F.F., 1979. Summary of information and potential downstream effects of hydro-electric development on the Liard River. B.C. Hydro Liard Hydroelectric Project Studies, Report from F.F. Slaney & Co. Ltd., Vancouver to B.C. Hydro, Vancouver, B.C., 5 volumes

SMITH, M.W., 1981. Effects of break-up changes on microclimate and bioclimate in the Mackenzie Delta: initial assessment and study suggestions. Carleton University, Ottawa, Report to B.C. Hydro, Vancouver, B.C.

TAYLOR, J., S. McCORMACK, K. ENGLISH and A. SEKERAK, 1982. Fisheries and limnological studies in selected lakes in the Mackenzie Delta, 1981. B.C. Hydro Liard Hydroelectric Project Studies, Report from LGL Ltd., Sidney to B.C. Hydro, Vancouver, B.C., 240 pp.

WELCH, C.E., D.F. PENNER, J.A. DUNCAN and P.S. JALKOTZY, 1984. Studies on muskrat ecology in the Mackenzie Delta, 1982-1983. Report by McCourt Management Ltd. to B.C. Hydro, Vancouver, B.C.

WYBORN, M., 1982. Liard River hydro-electric development: a review of water temperature sensitivity of beluga whales. B.C. Hydro Liard Hydroelectric Project Studies, Report ESS-47, Environmental and Socio-Economic Services Department, B.C. Hydro, Vancouver, B.C., 26 pp.

THE IMPACTS OF CLIMATIC VARIABILITY AND CHANGE IN THE MACKENZIE DELTA

R.G. Lawford[1] and S.J. Cohen[2]

[1]Hydrometeorological Research Division
Canadian Climate Centre
11 Innovation Boulevard
Saskatoon, Saskatchewan
S7N 3H5   CANADA

[2]Arctic Section
Analysis and Impact Division
Canadian Climate Centre
4905 Dufferin Street
Downsview, Ontario
M3H 5T4   CANADA

ABSTRACT

Emissions of carbon dioxide, methane and other radiatively-active trace gases have led to increased atmospheric concentrations. Experiments with atmospheric General Circulation Models (GCM) indicate that if trace-gas concentrations were to increase to the radiative equivalent of a doubling of carbon-dioxide concentrations, the so-called greenhouse effect would strengthen and global climate would experience unprecedented warming. Most scenarios derived from GCMs indicate that for the above increase in trace gases, global mean annual temperatures would warm by 1.5 to 5.0°C by the middle of the 21st century.

At regional and seasonal scales, projections have been outside this range, with much greater warming and generally higher precipitation projected for high latitudes in winter. The Canadian Arctic, including the Mackenzie Delta, would be one of those regions experiencing this change. There is much uncertainty associated with these models, particularly in their ability to provide regional-scale information. However, if this change were to occur as projected, what would be the implications for the Delta?

One possible scenario would see the Delta's hydrology experience shifts in its seasonal cycle. Streamflow would peak earlier and at a higher volume, while increased evapotranspiration during the longer growing season would lead to lower minimum flow in late-summer and fall. Lake levels would be similarly altered. There would also be decaying permafrost, reductions in ice cover, changes in vegetation species and extent, all of which could affect the Delta's hydrology and ecology. Breeding and migration patterns would probably change.

An additional factor would be the influence of sea-level rise. The Delta's coastline is already submerging, and it would accelerate under this scenario. This could result in greater coastal erosion, and increased penetration of saline water into the Delta during low-flow periods.

The above represents only a rough qualitative picture of the future. What is needed is a long-term multidisciplinary research effort into the impacts of climate-warming scenarios on the Delta's hydrology and ecology.

INTRODUCTION

The Mackenzie Delta is a unique environment shaped by the hydrology and, in turn, by the climate of the area. Climate is the major driving force in the variability and changes which are observed in the Delta. Temperature regimes govern the distribution of permafrost and thermokarst processes. Precipitation patterns govern the run-off in the Delta. The volume of run-off entering the Delta is determined by temperature and precipitation regimes in the upstream basin. During the past century, temperature and precipitation have fluctuated about relatively constant means. However, recent research regarding the effects of increasing atmospheric concentrations of carbon dioxide and other radiatively-active gases on the climate indicate that the long-term mean temperature and, possibly, mean precipitation may be changing. Furthermore, the variability of temperature and precipitation about these means may also be altered. The following paper discusses the implications of such changes for the Mackenzie Delta and reviews the types of analyses and studies required to examine these hypotheses.

CLIMATIC VARIABILITY IN THE MACKENZIE DELTA

The Seasonal Cycle

Measurements of temperature and precipitation in the Delta started in 1940 at Aklavik and continued to 1960. Observations began in 1957 at Inuvik and have continued to the present. The seasonal distribution of temperature for Inuvik is shown in Figure 1a. The relatively high temperatures in the summer for such a northern latitude are the result of the long hours of daylight during June and July. The seasonal distribution of monthly precipitation shows a maximum of precipitation in the month of August at Inuvik (see Figure 1b) and a maximum between July and August at Aklavik. During July and August precipitation amounts reach a maximum because the storms tend to track over the delta area. The distributions also show secondary maxima in October, presumably associated with the peak occurrence of winter storms. The precipitation amounts in each month are not high, consequently the amount of evaporation in the summer exceeds the summer and even the annual precipitation totals.

The Thornthwaite model was used to compute evapotranspiration at Inuvik using current climatic normals. It should be noted that the results of this model may be in error for a permafrost environment such as the Delta because the coefficients in the model apply to a more southern environment. However, since the results were being used for comparative purposes only it was felt that the computations still had some value. According to these calculations the annual potential evapotranspiration is 454 mm while the annual precipitation at Inuvik is 266 mm and at Aklavik 207 mm. The actual evapotranspiration is somewhat less than the potential evapotranspiration.

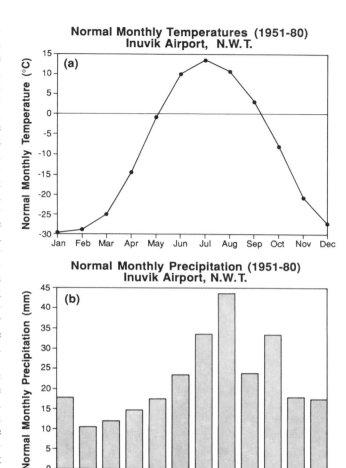

Figure 1a. *Monthly mean temperatures for Inuvik.*
Figure 1b. *Monthly mean precipitation amounts for Inuvik.*

Synoptic Controls

The pressure patterns accompanying the seasons in the Arctic have been described by Walsh and Chapman (1990). As shown in Figure 2, Mean Sea Level (MSL) pressures occur over the Pacific and higher pressures prevail over the Northwest Territories during the winter months. By July this pattern reverses itself

Lawford and Cohen

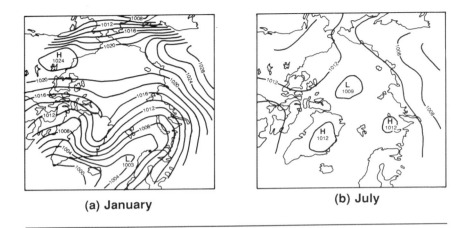

(a) January	**(b) July**

Figure 2. Surface monthly mean pressure patterns.

with lower pressures over the Arctic Ocean. During the spring and fall, a weak high-pressure cell exists over the Arctic with lower pressures again dominating over the Pacific. The pressure pattern suggests that there is a general flow from the northwest for most of the year.

Trends and Interannual Variability

Precipitation and temperature patterns vary from year-to-year. Major trends in the annual temperature patterns indicate that a warming has taken place over the Yukon and the western parts of the Northwest Territories. The trends for specific stations are shown in Figures 3 and 4. In Inuvik (Figure 3) the mean temperatures for the year and the summer showed little variation. The warming trend is more evident for January. January temperatures began warming in the 1970s reaching a monthly average high of -13°C in 1981. At Whitehorse, where a longer record exists (see Figure 4), a marked warming of winter temperatures began in 1973. Although less dramatic, the trends are also evident in the annual mean temperature.

The annual precipitation amounts have also shown significant variability with totals ranging from 180 to 360 mm·yr^{-1} for Inuvik. However, there is no clearly identifiable trend in precipitation amounts. It has been argued by some that the 1980s are a period when the early signs of a climatic warming have first become detectable. According to Figure 3 the warmest mean annual temperatures at Inuvik occurred in the late 1970s. Further south, at latitudes of 60 to 65°N, the warmer temperatures occurred after 1980. It would be the authors' view that while the observed temperature trends are not conclusive evidence that global warming is taking

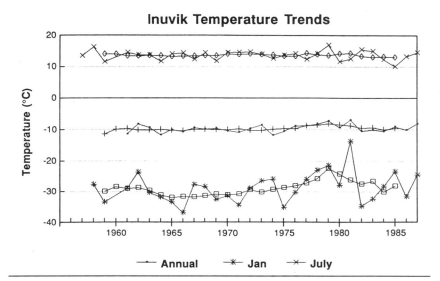

Figure 3. Trends in annual, January, and July mean temperatures for Inuvik.

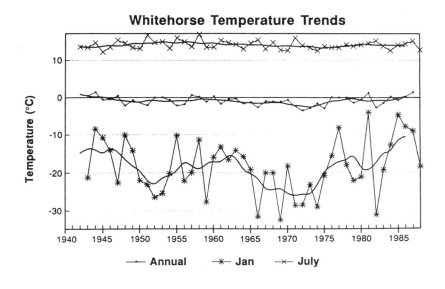

Figure 4. Trends in annual, January, and July mean temperatures for Whitehorse.

Lawford and Cohen

place, they are consistent with what would be expected with a warming scenario. In addition, the fact that the largest temperature increases occurred at different latitudes during different years suggests that the year-to-year variations in temperature in the Mackenzie Delta are dependent on the changes in the atmospheric circulation patterns over the Arctic. Consequently, it is reasonable to expect that some of the first signs of a climatic warming, either through changes in the local radiation balance or in the atmospheric circulation, will be seen in the Delta.

CLIMATE CHANGE ON A LOCAL AND REGIONAL SCALE

Global-Warming Scenarios

The issue of global warming is one that is of major concern for regional developers. Clearly, a warmer climate will influence the Delta significantly. Similarly a global warming will impact on other regions. In recognition of these complexities, the World Climate Programme, was established in 1979. It includes the World Climate Impacts Programme which has three main areas of responsibility: a) climate impact-assessment methods, b) impacts of anthropogenic climate change, and c) impacts of climate variation on food production (WMO, 1979). Emerging from this is a relatively new field of study commonly known as "climate impact assessment".

There are differences between the temporal and spatial scales of global climate warming and changes in regional environmental and economic systems. For example, there are different levels of flexibility and response times of managed and unmanaged resource systems (Clark, 1985). While the economic impacts of climate change will be felt most directly in industrialized areas, regions are not isolated and the impacts in relatively-remote areas such as the Delta will influence impacts nationally and globally. It is also necessary to shift from global-scale climate to regional-scale climate in order to look at regional impacts, and then to shift back to the global level to see how the "sum" of the various regional impacts create a picture of global impacts (Gates, 1985). This shift to regional climate requires consideration of the climate scenarios themselves.

There have been numerous attempts to model the thermodynamic response of the earth's atmosphere to a radiative equivalent of a doubling of CO_2 concentration (i.e., $2 \times CO_2$). Most scenarios derived from the more advanced Global Climate Models, (GCMs) indicate that global mean annual temperatures would warm by 1.5 to 4.5°C by the middle of the 21st century (WMO, 1986). At the regional and seasonal scales, projected changes have been outside this range, with much greater warming projected for high latitudes in winter and weaker warming projected for low latitudes all year (Jaeger, 1988).

Many uncertainties exist at the regional scale (e.g., Grotch, 1988). While the major features of the global circulation are reproduced in a $1 \times CO_2$ simulation (i.e., present climate) there are errors in the location of circulation features during particular times of the year. For impacts work, we assume some confidence in the ability of GCMs to be sensitive to changes in forcing factors (e.g., atmospheric trace-gas concentrations) and to project global-scale changes of temperature and other "basic" parameters, but there is a preference to use station observations as the baseline for the 1 x CO_2 conditions until GCMs show greater reliability. Thus, the climate projection (i.e., scenario) is a composite of the GCM-projected anomaly "added" to a "normal" obtained from station observations.

This approach was followed by the International Institute for Applied Systems Analysis (Parry *et al.*, 1988) and the U.S. Environmental Protection Agency (Smith and Tirpak, 1990) in major studies of regional impacts. Kellogg and Zhao (1988) note that this is reasonable for a parameter like temperature, but not for soil moisture which is dependent on many atmospheric and landscape factors (e.g., precipitation, evapotranspiration, run-off, soil, land use) and its distribution is less well known. Neither of the above major projects used GCM soil-moisture output. Most of the case studies within these projects computed hydrological parameters separately using temperature and precipitation output from GCMs.

The range of uncertainty may be different from the range of scenario results. However, at the moment, there is no objective way to measure uncertainty or to assign a probability to any global-warming scenario. For example, in an attempt to assess the ability of two GCMs to simulate temperature variability, Mearns (1990) concluded that neither of these GCMs could be rated as "better" for assessing changes in variability. Another study (Kellogg and Zhao, 1988) attempted to measure signal-to-noise ratios and statistical-significance levels of GCM soil-moisture output, but the authors concluded that such measures could not be used to judge the models' relative merits. Such a judgement could not be made at the regional scale either (e.g., Grotch, 1988; R. Wong, Alberta Research Council, pers. comm.).

Despite the uncertainties associated with these models, particularly in their ability to project regional-scale changes, the consensus regarding the global-scale warming, which could occur at an unprecedented rate and magnitude (WMO, 1986), has led to scientific and political concern regarding the possible impacts of this change on natural and social systems at global and regional scales (e.g., WMO, 1988).

A wide range of possible arctic impacts have been described by Maxwell and Barrie (1989). This information has been used to produce a simplified framework for an integrated assessment of climate-change impacts in the Canadian Arctic (Figure 5). This figure illustrates a number of linkages between climate, the physical and biological environments, resource users and the economy. For example, impacts research on transportation requires consideration of direct linkages between climate, hydrology and snowcover, and the indirect influences of permafrost and vegetation.

Before approaching the various components of the above (or other) framework, it is useful to place this effort in the broader context of climate-related research. What is the "mission" of regional impacts work? Perhaps the primary goal is to bring global-climate issues to the regional level in an objective and quantitative

Lawford and Cohen

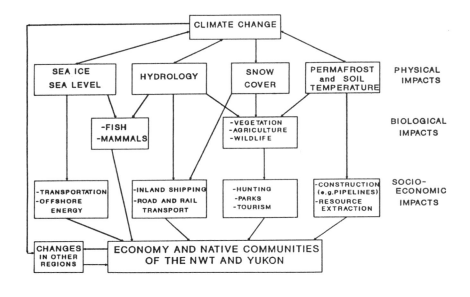

Figure 5. Framework for the integrated assessment of climate change impacts in the Canadian Arctic.

manner, thereby counteracting extremist rhetoric and encouraging grassroots involvement in research and development of response strategies. One of the major constraints is the availability of information, but there are others.

Our knowledge of linkages between climate change/variability, the environment and society, either individual sectors or entire regions, generally comes from the literature on impacts of past variations and extreme events (Kates *et al.*, 1985; Riebsame, 1988). Observations of past societal responses have also been used as a model for projecting socio-economic impacts by analogy (Glantz, 1988). However, impact of projected warming is an analysis of the future. In fact, this analysis is not just for the region being studied, since a definitive assessment of impacts in any region will frequently require assessment of linkages to impacts elsewhere (e.g., Smit, 1989). Will future linkages with climate be different from the past or present? It therefore becomes necessary to consider projections both of environmental conditions in other regions and non-climate factors at the global and regional scales. As Timmerman (1989) notes, non-climatic factors will not remain static. Global economic systems will probably change, as well as population, technology, feedback/ response mechanisms, and perception of environment and hazards. Attempts to provide "non-climate" scenarios have so far resulted in a wide range of possible futures, where the level of uncertainty is as great or greater than that for the climate-change scenarios. For example, scenarios of carbon emissions during the mid-21st century vary from a 60% decrease to a four-fold increase (see Bolin *et al.*, 1986).

In addition to these broad constraints, arctic researchers face the challenge of collecting data from a vast remote region where the human infrastructure is rapidly changing in response to global technological and economic trends, and decisions made outside the region. In the near term, one possible approach would be to include scenarios of climate and "non-climate" changes in impacts studies so that the sensitivity of the region could be investigated. While there is some industrial activity in the Delta, it could be expected that land subsidence and climate change and variability will be the major forces of change on the Delta's natural environment. This assumption could be significantly altered if the price of oil and natural gas increased thereby stimulating industrial activity in the Mackenzie Delta.

Warming Scenarios for the Mackenzie Region

Summary output from three GCM-based scenarios are shown in Figure 6. These were produced by the Goddard Institute for Space Studies (GISS), Geophysical Fluid Dynamics Lab (GFDL86) and Oregon State University (OSU) between 1984 and 1987 (respectively, Hansen *et al.*, 1984; Manabe and Wetherald, 1987; Schlesinger and Zhao, 1989). In comparing scenarios one must be careful to identify which version is being used. The GFDL scenario will be cited herein as GFDL86, since 1986 was the year of the model run. This is to distinguish it from earlier scenarios produced by the GFDL. Any research that utilizes outputs from these models should identify the scenarios by year of production (i.e., version) or specific reference, as well as institution of origin since the differences from one version to another can be significant. All three show conditions in the Mackenzie region. GFDL86 is warmest while GISS appears to be wettest. GISS, GFDL86 and OSU scenarios all show strongest warming during the winter (DJF). GFDL86 projects an increase of approximately 8°C for the mean annual temperature, which would raise it to near 0°C. The other scenarios are not as warm, but all show summer temperatures (JJA) exceeding 10°C, a critical threshold for delineating the extent of treeline and the boundary between boreal-forest and tundra climates.

Besides being warmer, the three scenarios are displaying increased precipitation in all seasons. However, the summer increases projected by GFDL86 and OSU are small, so if the higher temperatures result in actual evapotranspiration increases, it is likely that soil-moisture levels would decrease. Research on the regional water balance is needed to determine whether or not this would really occur in these two scenarios.

CLIMATE CHANGE ON A LOCAL AND REGIONAL SCALE

A global warming would be expected to influence the Mackenzie Delta and the surrounding region in a number of ways.

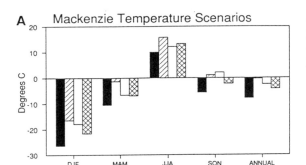

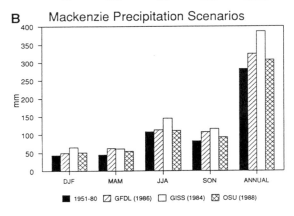

As has been noted in the work of Marsh and Hey (1988) and others, the flow in the Mackenzie River, particularly in the spring, is a critical element in the hydrology of the Delta. There are a number of perched lakes which tend to dry out over the summer months because evaporation exceeds run-off from the Delta. Run-off also determines the amount of sediment which will be transported to the mouth of the Delta and may contribute to the build-up of the Delta. Both the annual and the peak flows in the Delta are influenced by the accumulation of precipitation in the upstream basin. However the spring flow is a function of the amount of water coming down the Mackenzie River as a result of the spring melt and the ice jams which occur as the water moves along. Marsh and Hey (1988) also demonstrated that considerable variability can exist in the magnitude of the peak water levels (annual range of 3.52 m, average spring peak of 5.64 m a.s.l. over a 15-year period) although the timing of the peaks varies by only 13 days.

Figure 6. Summary output from three climate scenarios including the GISS, GFDL86 and OSU models for a) temperature and b) precipitation.

As described by Gerard (1988), Lawford (1988) and others, the spring break-up processes have both a dynamic and a meteorological component. The meteorological component involves the amount of radiation received at the ice surface and the ambient air temperature. The radiation is responsible for degrading the ice and making it more susceptible to break-up. The dynamic component arises from the force which the upstream ice and water are exerting on the ice at a particular point.

When the pressure of the ice is greater than the ice's ability to resist the pressure then break-up occurs.

Both of the above components will be sensitive to climatic change. With warmer temperatures, the ice formed during the winter months will not be as thick and strong, making it more susceptible to break-up as a result of the forces from upstream. The GISS scenario, discussed earlier, indicates that the amount of precipitation in the Mackenzie basin will be greater with increased snowfall accompanying climatic change. As a result, this scenario implies that there will be greater run-off generated in the upstream basin and hence, greater dynamic forces leading to break-up in the spring. On the other hand, the snow accumulation season will start later in the year and the snowmelt and peak flows will occur earlier. It is therefore difficult to determine to what extent climatic change will produce an increase in the peak flow although the overall annual flow is likely to be larger. Furthermore, if the thinner river ice is more susceptible to break-up, less force due to upstream ice/water pressure will be required to initiate the spring break-up. Consequently there is an argument for suggesting that the peak flows associated with climatic warming may not be as large as those experienced at present in spite of the heavier winter precipitation.

It is clear that we will not be able to give definitive answers until the linkages between climate and the spring break-up processes in the Mackenzie Delta are better understood. For this reason it is important to give priority to research linking the synoptic and atmospheric processes associated with break-up and the peak flows.

Permafrost

The existence of permafrost is a significant factor in the hydrology of the Delta. It greatly reduces the amount of water which can infiltrate the ground. Williams (1986) has documented the various processes which influence the surface-energy budget in permafrost areas. According to his summary, the amount of heat gained during the summer determines the depth of the active layer. Although physiographic parameters remain relatively constant from one year to the next, the meteorological factors such as cloud cover, wind, precipitation and temperature vary. Under climate-change scenarios such as those discussed in Section 3, which all arise from a reduction in the net radiative heat loss, one would expect annual energy gains from the surface for a number of successive years would lead to a reduction in the amount of permafrost both vertically and laterally.

Perhaps the greatest changes in the Delta could arise from these shifts. As the permafrost melts, the water holding capacity of the soil in the Delta and the amount of water which can infiltrate the ground will both increase. This could lead to a large increase in the loss of water from lakes through infiltration and increase significantly the ratio of dry-to-saturated surface. When the rate of thermokarst processes is altered by this warming, the edges around lake areas could slump leading to larger and shallower lakes. Changes in active layer thickness will also facilitate the growth

Lawford and Cohen

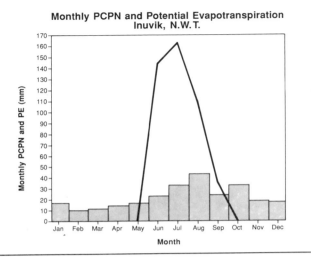

Monthly PCPN and Potential Evapotranspiration Inuvik, N.W.T.

Figure 7. Evapotranspiration and precipitation for Inuvik. The evapotranspiration was calculated using the Thornthwaite model.

of trees and other plant species which might spread into the delta area. The areas which will be first affected by this warming are those where ground ice is exposed to the atmosphere.

Lake Levels

Evaporation is a critical factor in the water balance of delta lakes. Without the replenishment by spring floods the lakes would have a net annual water loss because the evapotranspiration rates during the summer exceed the summer precipitation. Figure 7 shows the monthly values of potential evapotranspiration derived from the Thornthwaite model and precipitation for Inuvik. Because the average daily temperature for May is -0.5°C, the technique indicates that potential evapotranspiration during May is zero. The estimate is somewhat inaccurate because there are days in May when temperatures are above 0.0°C and evapotranspiration does take place. However, even this relatively crude computation shows that the water lost through evapotranspiration and evaporation is well in excess of the summer precipitation. Water bodies which provide a wet surface will lose water even more rapidly in the fall months when the water temperatures are warmer than the surrounding air temperatures.

Using the Thornthwaite model, the effects of a range of temperatures on potential evapotranspiration were also investigated. The results are shown in Figure 8. Based on this analysis we can conclude that the 1 to 5°C increase in the scenarios could result in an increase of potential evapotranspiration of 5 to 29%.

The lakes themselves are often formed as a result of the processes of sediment accumulation which can form a little dyke around the lake. As a result river levels have to exceed a certain value before water can enter the lake. As has been documented by Marsh and Hey (1989) many of the lakes in the Delta are of this nature. For the most part these lakes are relatively shallow. Unless they are replenished every four or five years with flood water they become so shallow that they freeze to the bottom in the winter and wildlife such as muskrat are unable to use them for habitat. With a global warming the muskrat may continue to survive because the lakes will freeze later and break-up earlier in the year. If the lake ice covers are thinner there will be a better chance that muskrat will survive.

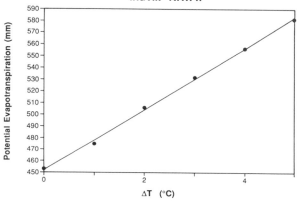

Potential ET vs Temperature Increase Inuvik N.W.T.

Figure 8. Changes in evapotranspiration amounts which could arise from a climatic warming of 1 to 5 degrees C.

Sea-Level Rise

Besides the continental influences, the Mackenzie Delta is also affected by changes in marine conditions. The Delta's coastline is already submerging (Egginton and Andrews, 1989) and this is probably allowing saline water to penetrate farther upstream. Since global warming is also expected to produce a rise in sea level, the question of coastal impacts becomes more critical here.

Sea level is expected to rise 0.5 to 1.5 m by the middle of the next century. For the Delta, a higher net change could be considered due to the ongoing submergence of the coastline. Higher sea levels relative to the Delta influence the effects of erosion along the delta land/sea interface. With global warming, the southern edge of the permanent ice in the Beaufort Sea will move further from the coast in the summer and fall months. With a longer fetch, high waves and extensive erosion events would occur for longer periods of time and, possibly, with greater frequency. Finally, possible changes in the marine climate, such as, longer ice-free seasons and more storms on an annual basis, could lead to changes in the frequency and magnitude of storm surges, causing more coastal erosion and allowing greater penetration of saline sea water during the summer and fall.

Sediment Loads

A critical influence in the evolution of the Delta is the sediment loading from transport by the Mackenzie River and deposition in the Delta. Sediment loading has been shown to be a function of run-off. If the vigour of the hydrological cycle and hence the run-off in the Mackenzie River increased due to global warming, the increased water transport combined with more active thermokarst processes could

Lawford and Cohen

lead to an increase in spring sediment loads. However, later in the summer lower river flows and possibly lower sediment transport could be expected due to increased evaporation from the upstream natural-storage reservoirs in the Mackenzie River network.

Delta Vegetation

A global warming is expected to shift the boundary of the boreal forest northward. Wheaton *et al.* (1989) showed that the extent of the expected shift is dependent on the doubled CO_2 GCM scenario on which one bases the projection. They found that the northern boundary of the boreal forest, which is associated with the 600 GDD isoline, would extend into the delta area under the GFDL86 scenario but would just lie to the south of the Delta under the GISS scenario. In either case there could be significant changes in the composition of the forest cover and other vegetation in the delta area.

The rate of response of vegetation to climatic warming is a subject of considerable debate. Some studies have indicated a very rapid migration of species. This issue, which is of significant concern because of its potential side effects on hydrology and wildlife, will not be easily resolved. Among the many research challenges that could be identified for the Delta, vegetation responses to climatic variability and change ranks as one of the most important.

FUTURE RESEARCH NEEDS

Based on this review of the possible impacts of climate variability and change in the Mackenzie Delta, it is clear that a number of areas need further research. Climate has played and will continue to play an important role in the evolution of the Mackenzie Delta. Unfortunately, the lack of data in the Delta limits our ability to describe the variability of climate and its effect on the state of vegetation and water resources there. More extensive monitoring and data archiving are required to address this problem. Because of the integrated impacts of climate variability on the hydrology and biology, certain sites may be particularly good locations for monitoring climate change. There is a need to identify highly climate-sensitive sites in the Mackenzie Delta and to establish long-term monitoring programs at these sites. Recent interest in climate-change detection and advances in technology (e.g., automatic stations) have led to the establishment of some new monitoring sites in the Arctic. These include the Canadian Climate Centre's four new permafrost stations, which have been providing climate and soil temperature data on an hourly basis (Etkin *et al.*, 1988), and a large number of new snow courses installed in the Great Slave Lake and Mackenzie River sub-basins (B. Latham, pers. comm., Department of Indian and Northern Affairs, Yellowknife). In addition, paleoclimate activities are generating more information about past climates, allowing us to place present trends in the context of longer-term variations.

The processes of change are very evident in the Mackenzie Basin. The Delta's expansion and contraction are governed by meteorologically-driven processes and the effects of the subsiding land. The water stored in the Delta's lakes is governed by the spring run-off which in turn is a function of the physical controls on the spring break-up and the precipitation loading on the basin. Although we know many of the linkages between climate and physical processes in the Delta in a qualitative way, they must be quantified and modelled if we are going to have a predictive capability for determining how the Delta might respond to climate change. Furthermore, the influence of climate-driven changes must be examined in the context of other physical changes taking place in the Delta.

Scale interaction is another important aspect of understanding the role of climate on the Delta. Some processes which occur with surprising regularity, such as the timing of spring break-up, are tied to large-scale geophysical and dynamic processes. In addition, considerable year-to-year variability is introduced by the small-scale processes. More research on the interactions of these processes is needed to identify how these processes, which operate on different scales, interact with each other and how they affect the Delta.

Predictions of the effects of global warming are further complicated by the fact that some factors will be sensitive to climate change and others will not be affected directly (e.g., amount of incoming solar radiation will not be affected directly while mean monthly temperature will be). The relative importance of these factors and their interactions must be understood and incorporated into models of climate/environment interactions.

The conduct of regional impact studies is a long-term interdisciplinary research issue, but the field is still in its infancy. In Canada, nearly 60 regional case studies using climate-change scenarios have been completed since 1984. Most of them were short-term efforts, in which climate-change scenario data were applied to a region using existing impacts models from various disciplines (e.g., hydrology, agriculture, etc.). In addition, extensive studies have been undertaken in the past showing how specific components of the environment respond to variations in the climate. Despite the time constraints, a number of regional sensitivities were identified thereby laying the groundwork for more extensive investigations. What is needed now are a small number of long-term regional studies that include model development. A recent attempt to develop a permafrost model that could be applied to the climate-change problem (Stuart, 1986) is a first step towards such an approach.

If our planet's climate warms, as the GCMs indicate, what will happen to the Mackenzie Delta? This unique region will undoubtedly experience a number of changes, but at this time only a rough qualitative picture can be provided. We need to place ourselves in a position that will allow us in a few years to provide a more complete answer to this question. Studies of environmental linkages with past and present climate variability would significantly contribute to this effort.

Lawford and Cohen

ACKNOWLEDGEMENTS

The authors gratefully acknowledge the assistance of T. Agnew in producing Figures 2 and 4. The opinions expressed herein are the authors', and are not necessarily those of Environment Canada.

REFERENCES

BOLIN, B., B.R. DÖÖS, J. JÄGER and R.A. WARRICK (Editors), 1986. The greenhouse effect, climatic change, and ecosystems. SCOPE 29, Scientific Committee on Problems of the Environment, John Wiley and Sons, Toronto, 541 pp.

CLARK, W.C., 1985. Scales of climate impacts. Climatic Change, 7(1), 5-27

EGGINTON, P.A. and J.T. ANDREWS, 1989. Sea levels are changing. GEOS, Energy, Mines and Resources Canada, 18(2), 15-22

ETKIN, D.A., A. HEADLEY and K.J.L. STOKER, 1988. Permafrost-climate activities within the Canadian Climate Centre. CCC Report No.88-7, Canadian Climate Centre, Atmospheric Environment Service, Downsview, Ontario, 92 pp.

GATES, W.L., 1985. The use of general circulation models in the analysis of the ecosystem impacts of climatic change. Climatic Change, 7(3), 267-284

GERARD, R., 1988. Climate data and ice jam forecasting. Proceedings, Third meeting on Northern Climates, 7-8 September 1988, Whitehorse, Yukon, 112-120

GLANTZ, M.H., 1988. Societal responses to regional climate change: forecasting by analogy. Westview Press, Boulder, Colorado, 428 pp.

GROTCH, S.L., 1988. Regional intercomparisons of General Circulation Model predictions and historical climate data. Report #DOE/NBB-OO84, Office of Energy Research, U.S. Department of Energy, Washington, D.C., 291 pp.

HANSEN, J., A. LACIS, D. RIND, G. RUSSELL, P. STONE, I. FUNG, R. RUEDY and J. LERNER, 1984. Climate sensitivity: analysis of feedback mechanisms. In - Climate Processes and Climate Sensitivity, J.E. Hansen and T. Takahashi (Editors), Maurice Ewing Series Vol.5, Geophysical Monograph No.29, American Geophysical Union, Washington, D.C., 130-163

JÄGER, J., 1988. Developing policies for responding to climatic change: a summary of the discussions and recommendations of the workshops held in Villach 1987 and Bellagio 1987, WMO/TD - No.225.

KATES, R.W., J.H. AUSUBEL and M. BERBERIAN (Editors), 1985. Climate impact assessment: studies of the interaction of climate and society. SCOPE 27, Scientific Committee on Problems of the Environment, Wiley, New York, 625 pp.

KELLOGG, W.W. and Z.-C. ZHAO, 1988. Sensitivity of soil moisture to doubling of carbon dioxide in climate model experiments. Part I: North America. Journal of Climate, 1(4), 348-366

LAWFORD, R.G., 1988. Climatic variability and the hydrological cycle in the Canadian North: knowns and unknowns. Proceedings, Third Meeting on Northern Climate, Canadian Climate Program, 7-8 September 1988, Whitehorse, Yukon, Atmospheric Environment Service, Downsview, Ontario, 143-162

MANABE, S. and R.T. WETHERALD, 1987. Large-scale changes of soil wetness induced by an increase in atmospheric carbon dioxide. Journal of the Atmospheric Sciences, 44(8), 1211-1235

MARSH, P. and M. HEY, 1988. Mackenzie River water levels and the flooding of delta lakes. NHRI Contribution No.88013, National Hydrology Research Institute, Environment Canada, Saskatoon, Saskatchewan, 39 pp.

MARSH, P. and M. HEY, 1989. The flooding hydrology of Mackenzie Delta lakes near Inuvik, N.W.T., Canada. Arctic, 42(1), 41-49

MAXWELL, J.B. and L.A. BARRIE, 1989. Atmospheric and climatic change in the Arctic and Antarctic. Ambio, 18(1), 42-49

MEARNS, L.O., 1990. Analysis of climate variability and extreme events. In - The potential effects of a global climate change on the United States, J.B. Smith and D.A. Tirpak (Editors), Hemisphere Publishing Corp., New York, N.Y., 17.1-17.45

PARRY, M.L., T.R. CARTER and N.T. KONIJN (Editors), 1988. The impact of climatic variations on agriculture. International Institute for Applied Systems Analysis and United Nations Environment Programme, Kluwer Academic Publishers, Volume 1. Assessments in Cool Temperate and Cold Regions, 876 pp.; Volume 2. Assessments in Semi-Arid Regions, 764 pp.

RIEBSAME, W.E., 1988. Assessing the social implication of climate fluctuations: a guide to climate impact studies. United Nations Environment Programme, Nairobi

SCHLESINGER, M. and Z.-C. ZHAO, 1989. Seasonal climate changes induced by doubled CO_2 as simulated by the OSU atmospheric GCM/mixed-layer ocean model. Journal of Climate, 2(5), 459-495

SMIT, B., 1989. Climate warming and Canada's comparative position in agriculture. Climate Change Digest, CCD 89-01, Atmospheric Environment Service, Environment Canada, Downsview, Ontario, 9 pp.

SMITH, J.B. and D.A. TIRPAK (Editors), 1990. The potential effects of global climate change on the United States. Hemisphere Publishing Corp., New York, 689 pp.

STUART, A., 1986. A spatial permafrost model for northern Canada and its application to scenarios of climate change. Canadian Climate Centre Report No.86-15, prepared by the Kel Research Corporation for the Atmospheric Environment Service, Environment Canada, Downsview, Ontario, 66 pp.

TIMMERMANN, P., 1989. Everything else will not remain equal: the challenge of social research in the face of a global climate warming. Joint Report No.1, U.S. National Climate Program Office, NOAA, Rockville, Maryland and Canadian Climate Centre, Downsview, Ontario, 61-77

WALSH, J.E. and W.L. CHAPMAN, 1990. Short-term climatic variability of the Arctic. Journal of Climate, 3(2), 237-250

WHEATON, E.E., T. SINGH, R. DEMPTER, K.O. HIGGINBOTHAM, J.P. THORPE, G.C. van KOOTEN and J.S. TAYLOR, 1989. Exploring the implications of climatic change for the boreal forest and forestry economics of western Canada. Climate Change Digest Report CCD 89-02, Atmospheric Environment Service, Environment Canada, Downsview, Ontario, 18 pp.

WILLIAMS, P.J., 1986. Pipelines and permafrost: science in a cold climate. 2nd revised edition, Carleton University Press, Ottawa, Ontario, 129 pp.

WORLD METEOROLOGICAL ORGANIZATION (WMO), 1979. Proceedings of the World Climate Conference: a conference of experts on climate and mankind. WMO No.537, World Meteorological Organization, Geneva, Switzerland, 791 pp.

WORLD METEOROLOGICAL ORGANIZATION (WMO), 1986. International conference on the assessment of the role of carbon dioxide and other greenhouse gases in climate Variations and associated impacts. Report of the International Conference on the Assessment of the Role of Carbon Dioxide and Other Greenhouse Gases in Climate Variations and Associated Impacts, 9-15 October 1985, Villach, Austria, WMO No.661, World Meteorological Organization, Geneva, Switzerland, 78 pp.

WORLD METEOROLOGICAL ORGANIZATION (WMO), 1988. The changing atmosphere: implications for global security: conference proceedings, 27-30 June 1988, Toronto, Ontario. WMO No.710, World Meteorological Organization, Geneva, Switzerland, 483 pp.

REGIONAL SEA-LEVEL CHANGES AND COASTAL RETREAT IN THE CANADIAN BEAUFORT-MACKENZIE REGION

S.M. Blasco

Geological Survey of Canada
Bedford Institute of Oceanography
P.O. Box 1006
Dartmouth, Nova Scotia
B2Y 4A2   CANADA

ABSTRACT

Radiocarbon dating of a limited number of recovered subseabed, peaty sediment core samples has resulted in a poorly-constrained relative sea-level curve for the Holocene time interval for the Beaufort continental shelf. This shelf has been dominated by a significant and continuous relative rise in sea level of approximately 65 m over the past 10,000 years. The rate of transgression has slowed to less than 0.3 m per century over the past 3,000 years. Erosion rates for the Beaufort coastline average 1 to 2 m per year but may range as high as 10 to 20 m at specific localities.

Global-warming models predict an acceleration of both sea-level rise and coastal retreat. Thermal expansion and melting of glaciers and polar ice caps are calculated to increase sea level by 0.3 to 3 m over the next century. Increased temperatures and northerly-shifting weather patterns may result in an increase in the intensity, frequency and duration of storms in the Beaufort-Mackenzie region. In response to more frequently occurring warmer summers and less severe winters, a less extensive summer sea-ice cover will result in more open water and greater fetch area. These four factors will combine to significantly increase wave energy, frequency and duration of occurrence, resulting in accelerated coastal erosion rates. Predicted increases in arctic summer temperatures of 2 to 4°C will increase the degradation rates of exposed ice-rich coastal permafrost cliffs and compound already accelerated erosion rates. In contrast, increased sediment supply to the Mackenzie Delta (resulting from a 50 to 100% increase in drainage basin precipitation and accompanying erosion) may serve to retard sea level and coastal retreat rates.

Production of oil and gas from Richards Island and the Beaufort nearshore zone may also compound sea-level rise and coastal retreat rates. Reservoir depletion may lead to settlement of production fields such as has occurred in the North Sea where the seabed in the Ekofisk Field area has settled an estimated 1 to 6 m in 15 years of production.

In a low-lying region such as the Mackenzie Delta where coastal relief is 3 m or less over large areas, the cumulative effect of natural change, global change and development may significantly accelerate sea-level rise and coastal retreat in the next century or less.

THE MACKENZIE AND GANGES-BRAHMAPUTRA DELTAS: A COMPARISON FOR PERSPECTIVE

M.L. Shome and R. Gerard

Department of Civil Engineering
University of Alberta
Edmonton, Alberta
T6G 2G7   CANADA

ABSTRACT

The intent of this presentation is to compare and contrast the characteristics of two deltas which, while they differ substantially in size and circumstance, have great significance for each nation for almost diametrically opposite reasons. Consideration of the differences and similarities is instructive.

The Ganges, Brahmaputra, and Meghna rivers form a single delta of some 70,000 km². This is one of the largest deltas in the world and is formed in one of the smallest countries of the world - Bangladesh. The hydrological regime of this delta is characterized by extremes varying from enormous floods to prolonged drought, the latter accompanied by salinity intrusion throughout the delta that exacerbates the problem. The coastal morphology of the delta and the tropical climate also combine to cause catastrophic floods of the delta lands due to tides and storm surges from the Bay of Bengal. Because the delta makes up the major portion of a country with one of the highest population densities in the world, it is intensively exploited for agriculture. The combination of extreme natural hazards and the high, and largely poor, population makes for frequent calamitous events.

In contrast, while still among the larger deltas of the world at 12,000 km², the Mackenzie Delta is very much smaller than that of the Ganges-Brahmaputra and makes up a tiny portion of one of the largest countries in the world - Canada. This delta has a quite stable hydrological regime with little variation in discharge and an offshore characterized by low tidal range and low energy. Being in a remote and inclement region, it is only sparsely populated. Instead of being a haven for people, it is a haven for wildlife, being one of the most productive and environmentally-significant regions of the North American continent.

These features of the two deltas combine to generate a striking similarity and a striking difference. Natural catastrophes and human population pressure keep the predominantly agrarian population of the Ganges-Brahmaputra delta poor while the quite different rigours of nature in the Mackenzie Delta impose similar constraints on the predominantly subsistence population. On the other hand, while the concern in the Ganges-Brahmaputra delta is with the effect of nature on human population and development, in the Mackenzie Delta the concern is with the effect of human development on nature.

INTRODUCTION

Deltas vary immensely in size, circumstance, and significance around the globe, their individual characteristics being a product of geomorphology, hydrology, and human utilization. The two deltas of concern herein are the Mackenzie and Ganges-Brahmaputra deltas. Their locations are shown in Figure 1. While both deltas are large, they differ substantially in size and circumstance, yet both have great significance for each nation for almost opposite reasons. Consideration of the differences and similarities is instructive. For example, the Mackenzie Delta plays a crucial role in Canada's arctic ecosystem and there is considerable concern that development activities in water resources, mining, and, particularly, oil and gas exploration and production could be detrimental to the delta environment. On the other hand, the Ganges-Brahmaputra delta supports one of the largest population densities in the world and the concern is with human survival, not environmental impact.

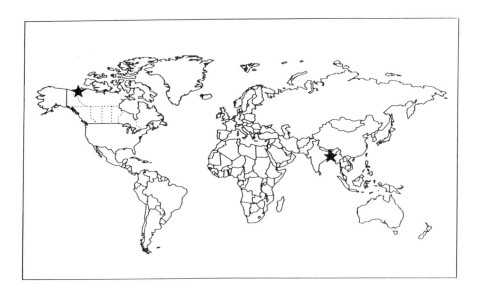

Figure 1. Locations of the Mackenzie and Ganges-Brahmaputra deltas.

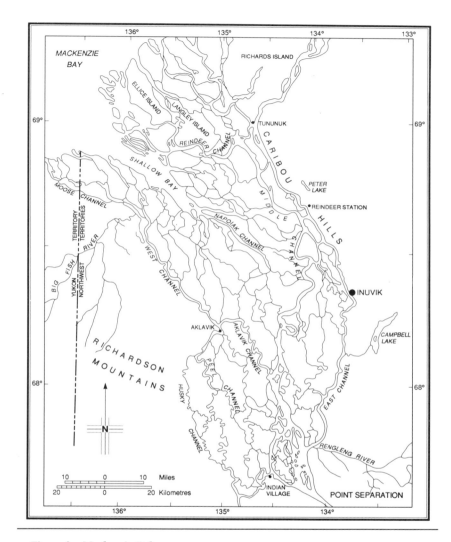

Figure 2. Mackenzie Delta.

GEOGRAPHICAL SETTINGS

The Mackenzie River drains one of the great river systems of the world and has formed a delta of some 12,000 km², shown in Figure 2. It is situated wholly within the Arctic Circle. Formed by the partial infilling of an old estuary, it extends northward from Point Separation at 68°73'N for roughly 200 km and over this distance

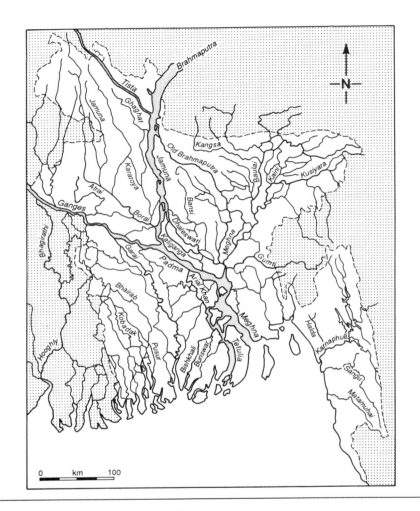

Figure 3. Ganges-Brahmaputra delta.

averages some 65 km in width (Mackay, 1963). It is a vast fan of low-lying alluvial islands with a maze of channels, cutoff lakes and circular ponds. The delta flood plain is bounded on the west by the Richardson Mountains, on the east by the Caribou Hills, and on the northeast by islands of fluvial and deltaic origin.

On an even grander scale, several of the largest rivers in the world - the Ganges, Brahmaputra, and Meghna - form the delta of some 75,000 km^2 shown in Figure 3, one of the largest in the world. This delta is located approximately between latitudes

21°N and 26°N. The Bengal basin, shown in Figure 4, of which the Ganges-Brahmaputra delta is a part, is bordered on the west by the Indian Shield and to the north by the Shillong Plateau, a large elevated area of Pre-Cambrian basement rocks. The eastern boundary is formed by the Tripura and Chittagong Hills and the southern boundary by the Bay of Bengal. With one of the world's major subduction faults in the north and a major transform fault in the east, the Bengal basin and its adjacent areas form one of the most active tectonic regions in the world (Morgan and McIntire, 1959).

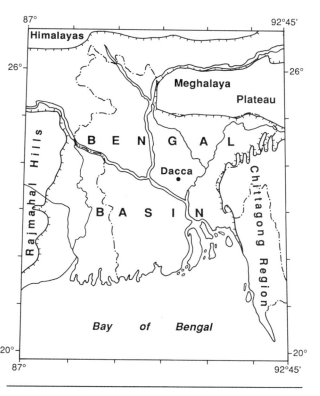

Figure 4. The Bengal basin.

CLIMATE

The climate of the Mackenzie Delta is characterized by short cool summers and long cold winters. Summer temperature maximums in the delta interior can range into the low 30s, while winter minimums may drop as low as -57°C. In coastal areas, the temperature range is less, reaching the high 20s in summer and around -50°C in winter.

Total precipitation is low throughout the Delta, varying from an annual average of 0.30 m at Fort McPherson to 0.16 m at Tuktoyaktuk. Rainfall is evenly distributed, averaging about 0.1 m over the Delta, with the maximum usually occurring in July or August. Snowfall decreases markedly from south to north, with Fort McPherson averaging about 2.0 m and Tununuk only 0.5 m annually.

The vegetation displays a northward transition from relatively dense subarctic boreal forest cover in the upper Delta to open tundra at the northern delta perimeter. The whole delta is in the zone of continuous permafrost.

Shome and Gerard

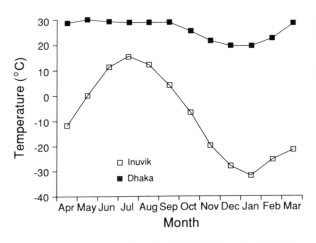

Figure 5. Comparison of the temperature regimes of the Mackenzie and Ganges-Brahmaputra deltas.

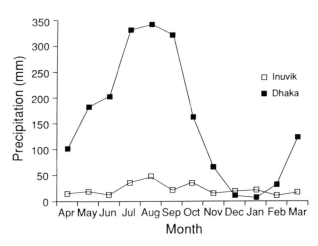

Figure 6. Comparison of the precipitation regimes of the Mackenzie and Ganges-Brahmaputra deltas.

In contrast, the climate of the Ganges-Brahmaputra delta is tropical with two distinct seasons of temperature and precipitation. The monsoon, or rainy season, extends from May to October, with maximum temperatures reaching over 30°C. The relatively cool and dry season extends from November through March, when maximum temperatures are about 25°C. Rainfall varies from an annual average of 1.40 m in the west to over 5.0 m in the north-east. Comparative plots of temperature and precipitation variation in the two deltas are shown in Figures 5 and 6, respectively.

HYDROLOGICAL ASPECTS

The Mackenzie River is one of the ten largest river systems in the world. The area drained by this river totals some 1,800,000 km^2 and is shown in Figure 7. The average and annual peak flows of the river are about 11,000 m^3·s^{-1} and 28,000 m^3·s^{-1} respectively (Neil and Mollard, 1980). The ice regime in the Mackenzie Delta spans approximately eight months of the year, with freeze-up and break-up being important phenomena in the lives of the inhabitants and the economy of the area. While the general hydrological regime of the Mackenzie Delta is quite stable, the detailed hydrological regime of various portions is complicated by the complex water distribution through an intricate maze of channels, lakes, and streams (Anderson and Mackay, 1973).

In contrast the hydrology of the Ganges-Brahmaputra delta is closely associated with monsoons and varies in the extreme. During the monsoon season the three major rivers carry enormous discharges, laden with heavy silt and sediment content,

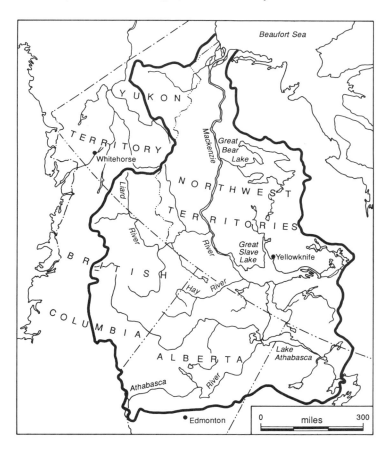

Figure 7. The Mackenzie River catchment.

Shome and Gerard

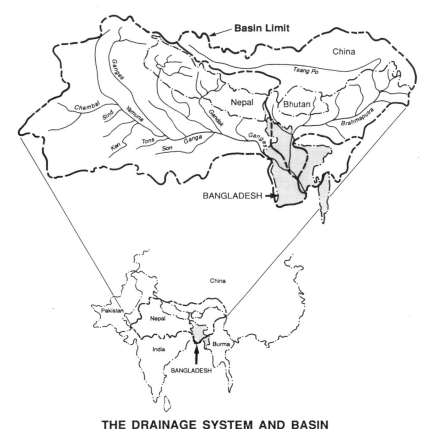

THE DRAINAGE SYSTEM AND BASIN

Figure 8. The Ganges-Brahmaputra catchment.

which cause widespread flooding. Tropical cyclones cause severe storm surges in the Bay of Bengal which exacerbate the problems. On the other hand, in the dry season the area is subject to prolonged drought.

The total catchment above the Ganges-Brahmaputra delta is shown in Figure 8. The Brahmaputra, with a catchment area of some 540,000 km^2, and the Ganges, with a catchment area of some 907,000 km^2, originate in the perpetual snows of the Himalayas and drain a large part of both the southern and northern slopes of that range. The Meghna, with a smaller catchment area of some 65,000 km^2, rises in the Luhai Hills of Assam (India) at a much lower elevation, but in an area subject to intense rains. The flow characteristics of the three rivers are given in Table 1.

Table 1. Flow characteristics of three major rivers of the Ganges-Brahmaputra delta.

RIVER SYSTEM	CATCHMENT AREA (km²)	ANNUAL AVERAGE FLOW	ANNUAL AVERAGE PEAK FLOW	ANNUAL SEDIMENT YIELD (million tonne per year)
Brahmaputra at Bahadurabad	540,000	19,700	64,800	608
Ganges at Hardinge bridge	907,000	10,900	51,100	479
Meghna at Bhairab Bazar	65,000	6,270	13,900	12

Source: MPO, 1986

The mean monthly discharge hydrographs for the main river systems of the two deltas are plotted in Figure 9.

Although not evident in Figures 2 and 3, there is another major difference between the two deltas: the Mackenzie is characterized by a plethora of lakes and ponds whereas few of these are present in the Ganges-Brahmaputra delta. This is likely due to the effect of permafrost in the Mackenzie Delta.

HYDROLOGICAL EXTREMES

Floods and Droughts

Floods in the Ganges-Brahmaputra delta are a complex and diverse phenomena. The main causes of flooding in this delta are excessive rainfall, drainage congestion due to flat topography, and the reduction of drainage capacity by siltation and floodplain 'management'.

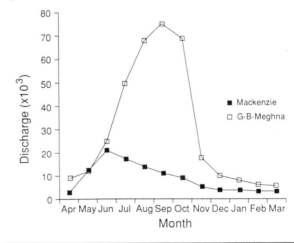

Figure 9. Comparison of the mean monthly hydrographs of the Mackenzie and Ganges-Brahmaputra Rivers.

Shome and Gerard

The effects of flooding on agriculture are by far the most important. Half of the land area is vulnerable to floods, which constitute one of the most critical development constraints in this area. The most severe flood in recorded history was that of September, 1988. It cost nearly 2,000 lives and inundated 2 million hectares of farmland. The heavy population density - an ironic testimonial to the fertility of the delta - worsens the impact of such disasters.

While floods disrupt national economy through inundation, droughts are a menace to food production through lack of water and salinity intrusion from the Bay of Bengal.

In the Mackenzie Delta, floods are less caused by large increases in discharge than by the obstruction of channels by ice jams in the spring under modest discharges. Break-up is usually accompanied by extensive flooding to a depth of about 1 m in the outer Delta. Far from causing catastrophe as in the Brahmaputra delta, this almost annual flooding is essential for the flushing and refreshing of the many delta lakes and ponds that are vital to the enormous wildlife resource of the Mackenzie Delta. Because of the water source, the steady hydrological regime of this river, the very low tides of the Beaufort Sea, and the lack of agriculture, drought and salinity intrusion are much less of a problem than for the Brahmaputra delta. However, any drastic change in the hydrological regime, such as may be caused by dam construction upstream, can severely disrupt the ecology of the Delta and have a drastic effect on the hunting and trapping activities which are the mainstays of the human population there.

Cyclones and Storm Surges

As indicated, another category of floods of a devastating nature along and near the coastal areas of the Ganges-Brahmaputra delta are storm surges caused by severe cyclonic storms. The majority of these storms have their origin in the Bay of Bengal, striking the east coast of India and the coast of the Ganges-Brahmaputra delta. The winds may exceed 220 km·h^{-1} (Murty, 1984).

Because of the high population density in the flat deltaic area north of funnelling tidal estuaries, it is not unusual for the storm surges caused by these cyclones to be calamitous. The largest national disaster of recent times was the cyclone of November, 1970, which had a maximum wind speed of 223 km·h^{-1} and a storm surge 4 m above normal high tide. It killed over 225,000 people and 280,000 head of cattle. Agriculture and property losses have been estimated at US $63 million (MPO, 1986). The most recent cyclone was that of May, 1985 with winds up to 154 km·h^{-1} and a surge 4.3-m high. This cyclone killed 11,000 people and 135,000 head of cattle and damaged 387 km of coastal embankments.

Only relatively modest storm surges are generated in the coastal areas of the Mackenzie Delta whenever strong onshore winds occur during ice-free periods. It is very common for large storms to inundate low-lying coastal areas to elevations in the order of 2 to 3-m above mean sea level. Two of the largest storm surges occurred in the Tuktoyaktuk area in 1944 and 1970; that of 1970 raised the water level more than 2.5-m above the high water mark, flooding low-lying areas and causing extensive erosion (Stewart, 1987). As the Mackenzie Delta is sparsely populated, the damage and losses are insignificant compared to those of the Ganges-Brahmaputra delta.

Salinity

The extensive coastal zone of the Ganges-Brahmaputra delta is subject to typical tide ranges of from 2 to 4 m, so that in the dry season, when river flows are low, penetration of saline water into the numerous estuaries can reach as far as 150-km inland. The upstream progression of saline water during low flow eliminates surface-water irrigation for a significant amount of land in the delta (MPO, 1986).

There is little information on the salinity characteristics of the Mackenzie Delta, but with the minor tides in this area (0.34 m), the region is unlikely to be seriously affected by salinity intrusion.

Erosion and Sedimentation

The main sources of sediment entering the Bay of Bengal through the Ganges-Brahmaputra-Meghna river systems are erosion products from the Himalayan watershed. The large discharge and heavy sediment load cause the river channels to be extremely unstable and to be constantly migrating laterally. The long-term patterns of river migration indicate that the Ganges has migrated eastward, whereas the migration of the Brahmaputra is westward (Coleman, 1969). Field measurements and airphoto interpretation show that the Ganges, Brahmaputra, and Meghna can migrate up to 60 to 1,700 m per flood season (Galay, 1980).

The estimated mean annual suspended sediment discharges at selected locations in the Ganges-Brahmaputra delta are shown in Table 1. The combined Bengal Basin rivers deliver some 1 billion tonnes of suspended sediment a year to the Bay of Bengal, yet map and photo comparisons indicate that the shoreline has remained quite stable (Coleman, 1969). Apparently most of the sediment brought to the Bay bypasses the bar and continues on into deeper water through an underwater canyon called the "Swatch of No Ground". This subaqueous delta is being formed in the deep water offshore that dwarfs one of the largest subaerial deltas in the world.

In the Mackenzie Delta, the rivers also migrate but not nearly so rapidly. In the southern Delta the migration rate is roughly equal to 1% of the channel width per year, while this figure is only of the order of 0.5% in the middle Delta. The average annual inflow of sediment in the Mackenzie River is about 150 million tonnes (Neil and Mollard, 1980). However, rather than building out into the

Beaufort Sea as expected, there is growing evidence that the Mackenzie Delta foreshore is retreating (Lapointe, 1984).

POPULATION

The Mackenzie Delta area is the centre of population, economic activity, and transportation facilities in extreme northwestern Canada, but it is sparsely populated. While the population is only about 8,000, giving a population density of less than $1/km^2$, there is over-population in relation to average income and employment opportunities. The basic economy of the Delta is founded on fur trapping, with the annual per capita income of the inhabitants of this delta being only about $2,000. This is a very low income relative to that in other areas of Canada. Furthermore the income from this activity depends on fluctuating market prices and the catches of fur-bearing animals, so the economy of the region is very unstable. However, the same hunting and trapping activities provide an abundance of 'country food', so the impact of the low income is somewhat alleviated.

In contrast, Bangladesh is one of the most densely populated areas in the world and the population has grown dramatically over the last thirty years. The total population of the country is now about 110 million, giving a population density of about $540/km^2$. The economy of the country is primarily dependent on agriculture, which provides about sixty percent of the gross domestic product. The per capita income of the inhabitants is among the lowest in the world, being about $179, and the people do not have the opportunity to supplement their income with country food. Hence this nation is suffering from a very much more pressing problem of over population and low average income than the Mackenzie Delta area.

COMPARISON AND DISCUSSION

The salient features of the Mackenzie and Ganges-Brahmaputra deltas have been outlined and are summarized in Table 2. It is evident the hydrological regime of the Ganges-Brahmaputra delta is characterized by extremes, varying from enormous floods to prolonged drought, the latter accompanied by salinity intrusion throughout the delta that makes the situation worse. The coastal morphology of this delta and the tropical climate also combine to cause catastrophic floods due to tides and storm surges. Because the delta makes up the major portion of a country with one of the highest population densities in the world, it is intensively exploited for agriculture. The combination of extreme natural hazards and the high, and largely poor, population makes for frequent calamitous events.

In contrast, while still among the larger deltas of the world, the Mackenzie Delta is much smaller than that of the Ganges-Brahmaputra and makes up only a tiny portion of Canada. It has a quite stable hydrological regime, with little variation in discharge, and an offshore characterized by low tidal range and low energy. Being in a remote and inclement region, it is sparsely populated. It is instead a haven for wildlife, being one of the most productive and environmentally-significant regions of the continent. At the same time the Mackenzie Delta area is a target for oil and gas exploration and production. Furthermore the Mackenzie basin is rich in water resources, especially for hydro-power. The concern is therefore that development of this resource will change the hydrological regime of the delta and thereby have a very detrimental effect on the delta ecology.

These features of the two deltas combine to generate a striking similarity and a striking difference. Natural catastrophes and human population pressure keep the predominantly agrarian population of the Ganges-Brahmaputra delta poor, while the quite different rigours of nature in the Mackenzie Delta impose the same constraint on the predominantly subsistence population. However, whereas the concern in the Ganges-Brahmaputra delta is with the effect of nature on human population and development, in environmentally-sensitive and generally prosperous Canada, the concern in the Mackenzie Delta is with the effect of human development on nature.

Table 2. Characteristics of the Mackenzie and Ganges-Brahmaputra deltas.

	MACKENZIE DELTA	GANGES-BRAHMAPUTRA DELTA
Location	68°N,139°W	32°N,90°E
Climate	Arctic	Tropical
Catchment area (km^2)	1,800,000	1,512,000
Delta area (km^2)	12,000	70,000
Average discharge (m$^3 \cdot$s^{-1})	11,000	37,000
Peak discharge (m$^3 \cdot$s^{-1})	28,000	130,000
Annual sediment yield (million tonnes)	150	1,100
Tide range (m)	0.34 D	3.6 SD
Population density (per km^2)	1	540
Annual per capita income	$2,000	$179

CONCLUSION

The main features of the Mackenzie and Ganges-Brahmaputra delta have been compared briefly, mainly to put the work in the Mackenzie Delta into an international perspective. The two deltas are the complete opposite in many ways, such as climate, hydrological regime and, especially, population density, yet both are characterized by a poor population in a continual struggle for survival. Nevertheless, whereas Bangladesh is preoccupied with simple survival of the population in the Ganges-Brahmaputra delta in the face of the severe threats posed by natural phenomenon such as floods, droughts and storm surges, in the Mackenzie Delta the preoccupation is with the ecological consequences of development, a luxury only a reasonably prosperous country could afford. The concern in Bangladesh is with the

Shome and Gerard

effect of nature on the people, but in the Mackenzie Delta it is with the effect of people on nature.

REFERENCES

ANDERSON, R.J. and D.K. MACKAY, 1973. Seasonal distribution of flow in the Mackenzie Delta, N.W.T. In - Hydrologic Aspects of Northern Pipeline Development, D.K. MacKay *et al.*, Report No.73-3, Environmental-Social Committee, Northern Pipelines, Task Force on Northern Oil Development, Ottawa, Ontario, 71-110

COLEMAN, J.M., 1969. Brahmaputra River: channel processes and sedimentation. Sedimentology Geology, 3(2-3), 131-239

GALAY, V.J., 1980. River channel shifting of large rivers in Bangladesh. Proceedings of the International Symposium on River Sedimentation, 24-29 March 1980, Beijing, China, Guanghua Press, 543-562

LAPOINTE, M.F., 1984. Mackenzie Delta channel dynamics: miscellaneous data. Northern Hydrology Section, Surface Water Division, National Hydrology Research Institute, Environment Canada, Ottawa, Ontario, 7 pp.

MACKAY, J.R., 1963. The Mackenzie Delta area, N.W.T. Geographical Branch Memoir No.8, Department of Mines and Technical Surveys, Ottawa, Ontario, 202 pp.

MORGAN, J.P. and W.G. MCINTIRE, 1959. Quaternary geology of the Bengal Basin, East Pakistan and India. Bulletin of the Geological Society of America, 70(3), 319-342

MPO, 1986. National Water Plan. Water Development and Flood Control, Ministry of Irrigation, Government of Bangladesh, 2 volumes

MURTY, T.S., 1984. Storm Surges - Meteorological Ocean Tides. Bulletin 212, Department of Fisheries and Oceans, 897 pp.

NEIL, C.R. and J.D. MOLLARD, 1980. Examples of erosion and sedimentation processes along some northern Canadian rivers. Proceedings of the International Symposium on River Sedimentation, 24-29 March 1980, Beijing, China, Guanghua Press, 565-600

STEWART, G.G., 1987. Flood hazard delineation and storm surge evaluation of Tuktoyaktuk and Kugmallit Bay: summary report, Water Planning and Management, Water Resources Division, Northern Affairs Program, Yellowknife, N.W.T., January, 21

THE EFFECT OF PEACE RIVER FLOW REGULATION ON INFLOWS TO THE MACKENZIE DELTA

L.H. Wiens

Inland Waters Directorate
Environment Canada
2365 Albert Street
Regina, Saskatchewan
S4P 4K1   CANADA

ABSTRACT

The primary objective of this paper is to assess the downstream effects of Peace River flow regulation on inflows to the Mackenzie Delta. When the gates were closed and Williston Reservoir began to fill in 1967, there was considerable interest in the hydrology of the Peace-Athabasca Delta which led Environment Canada to model daily flows through the delta for both the before and after Bennett Dam scenarios. Subsequent technical discussions in support of a proposed transboundary water agreement between Alberta and the Northwest Territories renewed interest in the downstream effects of Peace River regulation.

As expected, there was no significant change in the total annual inflow volume to the Delta. The results do indicate a slight but definite shift in the hydrograph of average annual inflows to the Delta, raising the average flow during the low flow months and lowering summer and fall flow values. Such an alteration of inflows could be reason for concern among wildlife and fisheries interests in the Delta. Additional regulations on major tributaries for the purpose of large scale hydropower production could further magnify the effects.

INTRODUCTION

Peace River flows have been regulated by B.C. Hydro's W.A.C. Bennett Dam since 1967 at which time the gates were closed and Williston Reservoir began to fill. Flow regulation had an immediate effect on the Peace-Athabasca Delta which has been the subject of almost continuous concern from that time to this.

In response to the interest in the hydrology of the Peace-Athabasca Delta, Environment Canada modelled daily flows through the delta under both natural and regulated flow conditions, for the period 1960 to 1984. Natural flows represent the flow conditions that existed before Bennett Dam began operation while regulated flows reflect flow conditions under the influence of Bennett Dam operation. As a result of the Peace-Athabasca Delta studies, two sets of flow files were created for the location of the Water Survey of Canada (WSC) hydrometric station on the Slave

River at Fitzgerald. The flow files represented the regulated and natural daily outflows from the Peace-Athabasca Delta model for the period 1960 to 1984.

Further interest in the downstream effect of Peace River flow regulation arose out of technical discussions in support of a proposed transboundary waters agreement between Alberta and the Northwest Territories. Environment Canada began a downstream effects study based on the two sets of daily outflow files from the Peace-Athabasca Delta work. The results of a portion of that study provide the material which is the subject of this paper.

Although the work of the downstream effects study has not been officially documented to date, it was felt that the preliminary information on Mackenzie Delta inflows was of sufficient value to be released at this time. Various disciplines with study interests in the Mackenzie Delta can profit from the knowledge that there has been a slight shift in the magnitude of delta inflows. Furthermore, the generalized results of this study can serve as an indicator on which to base estimates of the effect that future upstream developments might impose on the hydrology of the Delta.

FLOW ROUTING

The object of the downstream effects study was to route the regulated and natural Slave River flows downstream to various points of interest on the Mackenzie River for comparison purposes. Flow routing was carried out using a computer program developed by Environment Canada, known as the SIMPAK (Canada, Environment Canada, 1979) model. The model is based on the routing portion of the SSARR model which uses the Puls Method to route the daily flows downstream. A similar technique is used to route flows through Great Slave Lake. A more detailed description of the routing technique can be found in the User Manual, previously mentioned. The last study point on the Mackenzie River was at the location of the WSC hydrometric station above Arctic Red River.

RESULTS

The results of the work are presented in terms of monthly mean values of the maximum, mean, and minimum flows as illustrated graphically in Figure 1.

The total annual inflow volume to the Delta has not been altered, but there has been a definite shift in the annual hydrograph. In general, winter flows appear to have increased, on the average, while the annual recession flows are somewhat lower than under natural flow conditions.

It appears that the operation of Bennett Dam has resulted in an average flow increase of 20 to 30% to the Delta during the low-flow months. In particular, minimum flows have been raised significantly in the months of February to May. Conversely, summer and fall flows have diminished by as much as 5 to 10%. The

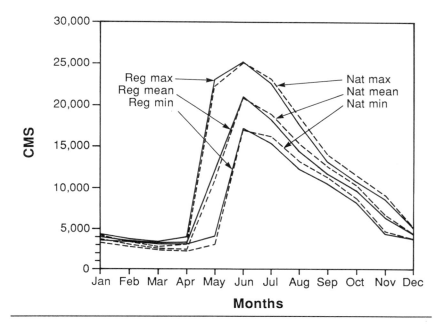

Figure 1. Mackenzie River flows above the Arctic Red River derived from monthly mean values for the period 1960 to 1984.

apparent decrease in minimum flows could be of concern to wildlife and fisheries interests in the Delta, especially in the months of July to November.

CONCLUSION

Additional control of flows on a major tributary such as the Liard could greatly modify the annual inflow pattern to the Delta. If the purpose of regulation is for large-scale hydro-power production the effect will further intensify the effects indicated in this study.

REFERENCES

CANADA, ENVIRONMENT CANADA, 1979. SIMPAK computer program users manual. Water Planning and Management Branch, Inland Waters Directorate, Pacific and Yukon Region, Environment Canada, Vancouver, B.C.

LIST OF PARTICIPANTS

Dr. Chris R. Burn
Department of Geography
University of British Columbia
2170 - 1984 West Mall
Vancouver, British Columbia
V6T 1W5   CANADA

Dr. Ken Chang-Kue
Department of Fisheries and Oceans
Freshwater Institute
501 University Crescent
Winnipeg, Manitoba
R3T 2N6   CANADA

Dr. Larry D. Cordes
Department of Geography
University of Calgary
2500 University Drive North
Calgary, Alberta
T2N 1N4   CANADA

Mr. Andre Dentremont
Environmental Quality Division
Environment Protection
Environment Canada
Yellowknife, Northwest Territories
X1A 2B5   CANADA

Dr. T. Milne Dick
National Hydrology Research Institute
11 Innovation Boulevard
Saskatoon, Saskatchewan
S7N 3H5   CANADA

Dr. H. Loney Dickson
Canadian Wildlife Service
Environment Canada
4999 - 98th Avenue, 2nd Floor
Edmonton, Alberta
T6B 2X3   CANADA

Ms. Mary Ferguson
Environmental Sciences Division
National Hydrology Research Institute
11 Innovation Boulevard
Saskatoon, Saskatchewan
S7N 3H5   CANADA

Dr. Larry Gerard
Department of Civil Engineering
University of Alberta
Edmonton, Alberta
T6G 2G7   CANADA

Dr. Robert E. Hecky
Department of Fisheries and Oceans
Freshwater Institute
501 University Crescent
Winnipeg, Manitoba
R3T 2N6   CANADA

Dr. Raymond H. Hesslein
Department of Fisheries and Oceans
Freshwater Institute
501 University Crescent
Winnipeg, Manitoba
R3T 2N6   CANADA

Ms. Kimberley A. Jenner
Present Address:
Deltamarine Consulting
13 Elizabeth Street
Dartmouth, Nova Scotia
B2W 2T4   CANADA

Mr. Brian Latham
Northern Affairs
Box 1500
Yellowknife, Northwest Territories
X1A 2R3   CANADA

Mr. Richard G. Lawford
Hydrometeorological Research Division
Canadian Climate Centre
11 Innovation Boulevard
Saskatoon, Saskatchewan
S7N 3H5   CANADA

Dr. Lance F.W. Lesack
Present Address:
Department of Geography
Simon Fraser University
Burnaby, British Columbia
V5A 1S6   CANADA

193

Mr. Peter LEWIS
1212 Duke Street
Victoria, British Columbia
V8P 2B6   CANADA

Dr. Philip MARSH
Hydrological Sciences Division
National Hydrology Research Institute
11 Innovation Boulevard
Saskatoon, Saskatchewan
S7N 3H5   CANADA

Mr. Greg MCCULLOUGH
Department of Fisheries and Oceans
Freshwater Institute
501 University Crescent
Winnipeg, Manitoba
R3T 2N6   CANADA

Dr. Langley R. MUIR
Office of Energy Research and
Development
580 Booth Street
Ottawa, Ontario
K1A 0E4   CANADA

Dr. Wally NICHOLAICHUK
Hydrological Sciences Division
National Hydrology Research Institute
11 Innovation Boulevard
Saskatoon, Saskatchewan
S7N 3H5   CANADA

Mr. Tom OLSON
Saskatchewan Water Corporation
3rd Floor, Victoria Place
111 Fairford Street East
Moose Jaw, Saskatchewan
S6H 7X9   CANADA

Dr. Cheryl M. PEARCE
Department of Geography
University of Western Ontario
Social Sciences Centre
London, Ontario
N6A 5C2   CANADA

Dr. John POMEROY
Hydrological Sciences Division
National Hydrology Research Institute
11 Innovation Boulevard
Saskatoon, Saskatchewan
S7N 3H5   CANADA

Mr. Monas L. SHOME
Department of Civil Engineering
University of Alberta
Edmonton, Alberta
T6G 2G7   CANADA

Ms. Kirstie SIMPSON
Indian Affairs and Northern Development
200 Range Road
Whitehorse, Yukon
Y1A 3H2   CANADA

Mr. Andrew SMART
Inland Waters Directorate
Western and Northern Region
Environment Canada
1901 Victoria Avenue
Regina, Saskatchewan
S4P 3R4   CANADA

Professor Bill STOLTE
Department of Civil Engineering
University of Saskatchewan
Saskatoon, Saskatchewan
S7N 0W0   CANADA

Dr. Tony WANKIEWICZ
Hydrological Sciences Division
National Hydrology Research Institute
11 Innovation Boulevard
Saskatoon, Saskatchewan
S7N 3H5   CANADA

Mr. Jack WEDEL
#6 Cranbrook Bay
Winnipeg, Manitoba
R2C 0N9   CANADA

Mr. Larry WIENS
Inland Waters Directorate
Environment Canada
2365 Albert Street
Regina, Saskatchewan
S4P 4K1   CANADA

Ms. Susan WILKINS
Sigma Engineering Limited
800 - 1176 West Georgia Street
Vancouver, British Columbia
V6E 4A2   CANADA

Mr. Herb WOOD
Inland Waters Directorate
Environment Canada
P.O. Box 1693
Inuvik, Northwest Territories
X0E 0T0   CANADA